SHOAL

SHOAL

A THANET WRITERS ANTHOLOGY

EDITED BY

ALICE OLIVIA SCARLETT

SHOAL
Paperback ISBN: 978 1 912673 00 1
eBook ISBN: 978 1 972673 50 6

Published by Thanet Writers
4 Cedar Close, Margate, Kent CT9 2TS

This First Edition published by Thanet Writers in May 2018
1 2 3 4 5 6 7 8 9 10

Edited by Alice Olivia Scarlett
Co-edited by David Chitty, Luke Edley, Hannah Fairbairn, Lannah Marshall, Seb Reilly and Connor Sansby
Selection © 2018 Thanet Writers CIC
Individual contributions © the contributors

Supported using public funding by
ARTS COUNCIL ENGLAND

Dedicated to the writers of Thanet, with thanks and pride.

Contents

Swimming Against the Tide

FOREWORD BY
DAVID LEE STONE

WRITING IS A BUSINESS OF OPINIONS AND unfortunately, if you're an aspiring writer, it's invariably one initial opinion that will either make your dreams come true or break your heart.

The worst day of my writing career started really well. The late, great Terry Pratchett had given me all the advice I needed in order to meet with one of the most powerful and influential editors in England and I had arguably the two best agents in the business, Sophie Hicks and Ed Victor, watching my back: everything was going my way.

Two hours later, I was standing on a bridge with the manuscript for my debut novel in my hands, crying my eyes out and wondering what went wrong. It wasn't the horrible, stinging comments the man had made or the casual way he'd singled out all my favourite creative inventions for derision: it was the suggestion that I drop the book completely and write it off as a bad idea.

Write it off.

I was 22 years old at the time and if I'd done that, I would have been writing off the entirety of my teenage years: the girlfriend I'd never had, the friends who had slowly walked away when I chose to stay in and write rather than go out and have fun, the mum who'd worked three jobs so I could try to make it as a writer when most of the extended family saw me as a dreaming fool and a complete waste of space. You see, I'd been submitting manuscripts to publishers since I was twelve years old.

I didn't write the book off and eighteen months later I became, very briefly, the highest paid author in the world. In the media frenzy that followed—spearheaded by a Times article entitled 'The Geek Gets Even'—the national press became so consumed with whether or not the book was worth the advances Disney, Sony and Hodder had paid for it that only one reviewer—Douglas Adams' biographer MJ Simpson— asked the question that actually mattered: was it worth £10.99?

Most of the critics decided that it wasn't: the series failed and it would be another decade before I broke into the children's bestseller lists with *Gladiator Boy* and *Undead Ed*. Sadly, all of the books I'm most proud of writing barely made their print run.

A week after I quit writing books in 2017, I went to my first Thanet Writers meeting. I did this because, already knowing one extremely passionate local writer (Matthew Munson), I wanted to see if I could find any other folks who might inspire me to carry on.

When I arrived, Seb Reilly was chairing the group and everyone was quietly reading the work of the first writer.

It was a positively encouraging, respectfully critical and deeply engaging experience. However, the biggest factor for me was the atmosphere: every writer sitting in that room absolutely loved what they were doing; the feedback on their own work, the enthusiasm to help improve the work of someone else.

I had nothing to contribute beyond a few notes on what editors and agents were looking for in the current marketplace and one or two tips about writing horror as I'd just worked on the panel for the World Horror Awards.

You need to watch Thanet Writers…and watch them very closely. I have a strong feeling that more than one of the authors in this collection is likely to soar to great heights and there is no greater support base than the people of Thanet. I will never forget arriving in Ramsgate town for my first book-signing at WHSmith—terrified that nobody would show up—to see the streets absolutely packed with people who wanted to help me succeed.

I thank every single one of you who did that for me. I'd also like to thank Thanet Writers as a group—and Hannah Fairbairn in particular—for continuing to give my work a local audience. Now it's time to read this wonderful anthology and throw your support behind all these other amazing writers. I will try to do the same.

David Lee Stone

Welcome to Shoal

INTRODUCTION BY
ALICE OLIVIA SCARLETT

HEY THERE. WELCOME TO SHOAL.

You're probably familiar with the image of a shoal of fish. A graceful ball of movement that dodges and turns and folds in on itself, a triumph of co-ordination and synchronisation where every little fish plays a part in making up the whole. Dozens of separate creatures with a common heart and goal, harmonizing and making something new and lovely together.

I think that picture really chimes with what this anthology is all about.

When the editorial team and I were organising the entries for Thanet Writers' first anthology, it struck me how much common ground all the stories shared. We hadn't set a theme, and we hadn't broadcast a specific subject we wanted people to write on, but still we could see the same threads running through every entry. Sarah Tait's 'Lucy,' a disquieting story about mothers and daughters. Maggie Harris' 'When the Flamingos Came,' a thoughtful tale of otherness and immigration. Lannah Marshall's 'Another Hot Chocolate,' a picture of melancholic victory over bullying.

Even the more out-there entries, like Matthew Munson's 'Life and Times of a Zombie' and Luke Edley's 'Cuke,' still hold at their cores those ideas about belonging, and family, and the fear of being outcast.

I think that's really interesting. Maybe it's simple serendipity, or maybe it's a sign about how humans are just writing the same things over and over again, trying to understand themselves and how they fit into the grand scheme of Life and Things, and how everything human boils down to these questions we so desperately want answered.

I don't know. But it's interesting.

Read the stories and come to your own conclusions. Either way, I hope you enjoy Thanet Writers' *Shoal*.

Alice Olivia Scarlett

SHOAL

First and Last, 1917

CATHERINE LAW

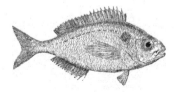

ON THE DAYS WHEN SHE COULDN'T LEAVE THE HOUSE, she watched for the soldiers coming home. Standing at the kitchen window, she could see the road pinned to the back of the peninsula, like a grey ribbon winding over marshes as dull as sheep's scat in winter, acid green in spring and now, at the end of summer, burnished like fool's gold.

The stranger appeared along the road, walking fast. She drew closer to the window pane to try to see him more clearly and the sharp morning sun made her squint. Gingerly touching her eye socket, she winced.

Last night, Ted's fist had had a conversation with her. For Ted was a meticulous man and, yesterday, he had been meticulous about salt. A pinch? Not enough. A spoonful? Far too much. She had ruined the stew and it had met with the flagstones, the crock pot shattered. He'd watched her get to her knees to extract the broken pieces, rinse them and set them out on the window sill to dry. Her mother had given her that crock pot. She tapped the shards now with her fingertips, remembering the violence of Ted's silence, his brooding stare. The bruises would keep her prisoner in the house for days.

3

In the past three years, she'd seen many men return on leave or for good: withered and stooped with dull hell in their eyes, wending their way past Ted's farm, the first and last house on the peninsula, depending on which way you were going. Home for the soldiers must be the fishing town, its harbour patrolled by gulls, for there was nowhere else to go if they came this way. If they kept on walking, they'd topple into the sea.

But this one? She opened the window. The first autumnal chill was sharp on her tender cheek bone. This one had not gone to war. She could tell by the confident set of his shoulders and the purpose in his stride as he made his way along the road towards her. He did not appear half a man like the others did. This soldier had been spared.

Ted had not gone either. Got away with it. Farming was exempt. He drank his way through the last three years as men he knew, men he didn't know, went to war and didn't come home.

The stranger was closer now, almost by the gate. Joy lifted her suddenly, as rich and as light as air. She ran to the door. She had not run in years. She had not called out in years.

'Harry!'

Harry from the school playground, Harry from dances in the town hall. Harry from the past, a time of childhood, when lamps were brighter, laughter easier. She shouted, his name hoarse in her throat.

'Is it you?'

He looked back over his shoulder. She saw him register her bruises, hesitate.

'Of course it's me,' he said, his never-forgotten smile brightening his face. 'But is it you?'

He came closer, his eyes growing opaque with memories. Cautiously, he stepped through the gate and walked towards her.

'So, you married him, then?' Harry weighed up the farm-house.

She nodded. Could say nothing else about it. Instead, she bade him come in, close the door. She asked him to sit in her husband's chair by the range while she made him a pot of tea. Harry from the school playground. Harry from the town hall dance. But, he corrected her, he had gone to war.

'I've been away for three years. Signed up with the rest of the fellows, in that first jubilant month. But now,' he said, and his eyes softened as they hooked onto hers, 'I'm almost home.'

She set the tea pot down, her hand shaking, the cups chinking as she rearranged them. It was unusual to sit drinking tea with a visitor at this time of the morning when there was housework to be done.

'You left the town quite suddenly,' she said, stirring her tea. 'I heard you went up to London.'

'Art school. Can you believe that? A boy from round here, indulging in that sort of caper.'

'I remember you, always drawing,' she smiled. 'You sketched me down by the harbour. Do you remember? And that painting of yours, that the headmaster put up in his study.'

'Probably still there, gathering dust,' Harry's laugh was a brief gasp. His face fell, became unreadable. 'But when the war came, I couldn't sit around painting. Had to do my bit. But I drew in the trenches. Couldn't stop myself. Pictures I can never show you, show anyone.'

'Perhaps, one day, Harry you ought to?'

His eyes roamed around her face. 'And Ted?'

She shook her head. 'Farming,' she said.

She stood suddenly, scraping her chair over the flagstones. She must get on. Ted liked his meals on time. She had stew to prepare.

'Would you mind,' said Harry, 'I'm not in any hurry. Can I sit a while, stay a while?'

All she could do was nod and turn her face away in case he saw the hot prickles of tears. And he sat quietly while she chopped mutton, sliced carrots, his presence comforting, his presence from a time of light and laughter.

She found her second-best crock, stoked the range until she had a good fire. There in her husband's chair, Harry seemed to have taken himself far away, his face quiet and peaceful. And she saw him as if for the first time, a young and vibrant boy.

'So, you married him?' he asked again.

The look on his face frightened her, for, reflected there, she saw herself and what she had wanted once.

6

'Please go now, Harry,' she said, fear making her angry. Ted might walk through the door at any moment. 'You must leave.'

Harry didn't argue, he simply understood, just as he had always done. Without a word, he walked to the door, his footfalls barely registering on the flags. In an instance, he was gone, and she thought that the sun had gone behind a cloud.

As the day drew on, and the stew bubbled away, she sat staring at the empty chair until Ted blustered in, newspapers under his arm, hat low on his brow, sniffing the kitchen air like a dog sensing something.

She hurried to the dresser to pour his ale. He sank his face into it and drank deeply, his legs outstretched, his boots stomped onto the fender. She busied herself around him, stirring the stew, boiling the kettle. He wouldn't look at her face, for then he'd have to witness what he'd done. Instead, he shook out the broadsheet, asked for more light and read. She'd have to wait until he had finished before she could ask to have a look.

The other paper that Ted had brought home, the local rag, was folded on the table; she decided to save that for Sunday when she might have more time to sit, more time to think. Watching the empty road from the kitchen window, she tapped her fingertips over the broken crock pieces on the windowsill. The afternoon was deepening, the sun sinking. She wondered where Harry was. At home, with his mother in the house by the harbour? Yes, by now, surely. By now.

'Lads from school. In the lists.' Ted tapped his newspaper, his voice a grumble, rising behind her. 'All from the same regiment. Wiped out. Bloody fools.'

Part of her crumbled at the thought of reading the relentless columns, part of her had ceased to be able to take it in.

'I'll look later.' Or, perhaps not at all.

'I need to bathe,' Ted said.

Out in the shed, she unhooked the heavy iron tub from the wall, lugged it back in, set it in front of the range and began to fill it with steaming water. Her back ached. As she bent over with the deadweight kettle, searing pressure tore inside her bruised face. Ted stripped, his white skin bright in the dim lantern light. She turned her back as he eased himself in to the water, then she took her position behind him, to wash him.

'What's in the pot?' he asked.

Mutton, she told him, speaking with difficulty. The intimacy of the bath muffled her words. She stared at the nape of his neck, at the dirt caught behind his ears and wondered if she had ever loved him, his skin, his hair, his eyes or his voice. As she had loved Harry.

'Not my favourite,' he said.

Her fist was a tight ball as she squeezed the flannel and trailed the water down Ted's back and he flinched, annoyed at her touch. He stood up in a rush of water and reached his hand out for the towel. She kept her eyes on the window as she held it for him.

'Mutton stew? My mother's was always better.'

He walked naked to the stairs. The ale had got the better of him and he'd sleep until supper time.

She turned up the lantern in the darkening room and opened the newspaper Ted had been reading. Her mind travelled along the road to the town by the sea, under the sky filled with seagull cries. She thought of other lanterns going on in other parlours, newspaper pages being turned, could ignore it no longer. She found the lists and began to read.

Who had Ted seen here from the Buffs? How many more of the town's boys were gone? Missing, presumed dead? Missing, presumed drowned?

Harry's name caught her eye because of a typesetting error. A letter in his surname was wonky, below the line. She stared at it and smiled. The military were wrong. They got things wrong, sometimes, didn't they?

But her stomach was a sluice of ice, a creeping chill at her core. She reached for the local paper and unfolded it. Harry was headline news. A photograph of him, in neat, tight uniform, looking just as she remembered, as happy and as fresh-faced as she had just seen him, sat there in her husband's chair. She wanted to laugh. He had looked well, so very well. Not as a man might do, who had just left the inferno of Passchendaele. Sitting by her hearth, he had looked young, as young as when he'd first left home, the town, her life.

She turned to the stew and began to stir. It was catching on the bottom. Ted would be furious. She wiped sweat from her forehead, flinching with pain.

Harry said he was going home. Home to his mother. He was compelled to do it. They all willed themselves elsewhere, from their stinking posts in the trenches, up to their waists in foul mud. And Harry had found her along his way. For how else would he have got there without passing her front door? And forcing her to remember. That he had been her first, and her last.

She plucked her coat from the hook and belted it tightly. She fitted her hat well onto her head, for the wind was picking up. Scooping up the pieces of the broken crocks from the windowsill, she poured them into her pocket. There was nothing else she needed. She folded both newspapers neatly, for that was how Ted liked to find them.

As she lifted the lid on the pot, she heard his snores through the ceiling. The stew was burnt, as she knew it would be. She picked up the salt cellar, tipped the lot into the pot, gave it a jolly good stir and shut the door quietly behind her.

The Pigeons

J A DUMAIRIER

THEY TROT ALONG THE STREET, THEIR HEADS BOBBING and nervous, as if they have lost their way amongst the parked cars. They are just looking to find some shelter, something that's away from the non-existent breeze that ruffles their coats, so they stop under a doorframe.

His hat is pulled down tight and it muffles his reddened ears and she has done the same even though the day is still warm and clear. She mumbles something incoherent, then takes another swig from her can of beer. He tries to explain how the government have ruined the country, but she can't see what he is trying to say. Not that it makes much sense to him out loud, but now he has spoken there's no way he would admit that he has got it all, everything, wrong.

Looking up he can see the silhouette of a tower block with signs plastered on it advertising offices to let. He tells her that they should rent an office as it's cheaper than a flat. At least then they could sleep in the warm. She replies, yes, and gazes off towards the horizon for a moment, then resumes her mumbling and asks for the end of his cigarette.

He takes one more long drag before passing her the measly remains that are still yet to expire. She holds it tight between her fingers and wraps them back around the can of beer. The cigarette embers still burn away and ash collapses from her hand.

She asks him for a smoke, now unaware of the smouldering filter that she holds, lost in drunken oblivion. He stares at her hand and laughs, but she still can't solve the riddle of what burns her fingers. He reaches down and looks inside, through the hole of the plastic bag for something to eat.

They've finished the tangerines that they stole from the supermarket; all that's left is a small cake. He unwraps it and devours it greedily. Still wobbling, she watches a pigeon land across the road. The tower casts a shadow over its tiny frame. She points it out to her companion and he tells her they and the bird are the same. It pecks the pavement. The cake in his hand feels heavy so he breaks a small piece off and throws it to the pigeon. She smiles. It's a traveller, he says, it's lost like us, a wanderer covering miles. A scavenger that lives amongst the rocks and steals to live. It's beautiful. They let it peck up all the cake. He sniffs and coughs.

She asks him for another cigarette.

Another Hot Chocolate

LANNAH MARSHALL

STIRRING MY DRINK, I WONDER WHETHER I'D HAVE paid for it if I'd known half of it would be froth. I hold back a grumble, pick up my pen, and try burying myself in a word search. If I were more adventurous I might try the crossword, but alas, that isn't for me.

There's a chill, but that's what happens when I get the last table. It's always the one by the door. In the summer it isn't so bad, but this is a patriotic March. Instead of bemoaning another patron's entrance, however, I wrap up and quietly celebrate having a seat at all.

Sure, there's the seat opposite me, but this is Britain and no one would dare sit on the same table as a complete stranger. That would be barbaric. The most hardened Brits would rather stand out in the rain than awkwardly park themselves with me, what looks to be a homeless woman giving evil eyes to a bountiful hot chocolate.

Another stir followed by the realisation that the bubbles are going to stay that way. I'm going to have to eat this thing like a yogurt. I'm halfway through when I stop.

I've found Hitler.

Scribbling out the dictator's name at the bottom of the page, I'm so pleased with myself I almost don't recognise the sound of a chair moving. Then I stop. My heart beats that little bit quicker, but I try to feign disinterest. If we just avoid eye contact then we can make it out with our esteems intact. The perfume is going to distract me.

"Evelyn?" she says, breathless and surprised. "I almost didn't recognise you."

I look up, bright-eyed with the biggest smile I can fake.

"Oh, what? Wow," I say to save time as I try to remember her name. Good luck with that, since I can't remember her face. In fact, I don't think I've ever met a woman as striking as the one sitting in front of me. Sure she's got a scarf wrapped around the lower-half of her face, but her eyes alone tell me she's something formidable. Never have I seen eyes so dark, sparkle so bright. Scrambling for names has turned into scrambling for words. Any of them. One of them at the tip of my tongue. Something other than the, 'a-bah-bah, lah. Wow,' I've got going on now.

She laughs. She laughs like I've been telling her a sweet story about a clumsy puppy, and I'm clamming up with sweat all over. I was not prepared for this. If I wasn't prepared for my disproportionate hot chocolate, I was not prepared for this.

"I'm Tabitha, um, Tabitha Clark from Cliftonville primary," she says. "Do you remember?"

I do. It seems passively and actively trying to erase those memories failed, but right now I'm glad it did.

18

March just got very warm all of a sudden, and I catch myself removing my rain coat. I'm too exposed, but all I can think about are my stupid clammy hands resting on my bouncing knees.

Crap, I haven't said anything.

"Y–Yes," I say and nod into my word search, my nose burying into a list of dictators. "You're the year below me."

"I'm sorry, I can see that you're clearly uncomfortable." That's a given. "But I wanted to say thank you," she continues. "And I'm sorry."

I look up.

"For what?"

For a moment Tabitha shifts around in her seat, and even starts to unravel her scarf, revealing her perfectly plush lips and sun-kissed skin. She fiddles with the cardboard of her takeaway cup, and then stops.

"When I was eight my sister, Denise, was in your class." Oh, her. "From what I've been told she gave you quite a hard time." Understatement of the century.

My body flushes up a new wave of a heat. A different kind with a surging passion that can only be quenched by a wicked tongue, but somehow I still it. Somehow I have it sit just behind my lips as I rest my gaze on Tabitha. As beautiful as she is now, it doesn't render her childhood legacy mute. She's innocent and doesn't deserve my wrath. At least, that's all I can tell myself as I sit back and take my half-a-hot chocolate like a shot.

"Yes," I say. "Not that it matters."

"It does matter," Tabitha says, leaning forward and giving me another whiff of her light perfume. There's no way something so earnest and sincere could be related to Denise. "I heard all the horrible things she did to you at school, and don't tell me she didn't."

"I won't."

"All the tricks she pulled, the people she manipulated and—"

"What's your point?" I ask, unable to stop myself. "You said you were thanking and apologising. This doesn't very much feel like either."

"Sorry, sorry, yes. I know." Seeing her suddenly fumble and look grieved has me silenced. "It's just, do you remember why she started targeting you so brutally?"

"Not really." I've never really paid attention to the things said and done in primary school. It was nearly two decades ago.

Tabitha straightens out, suddenly sure of herself, and clears her throat.

"It was because of me." The rest of the room feels strangely silent. I'm half-tempted to turn to check for spying eyes and half-tempted to run. Denise always sent people to do her bidding, to play mind games, to mess with me. The number of fake friends that were under her tutelage was beyond understanding, and I was labelled paranoid.

"Look, I don't know why you're here or what that sociopath wants from me—"

"Oh, I am so sorry!" she apologises, yet again. "I mean, she was picking on me first. At home. At school. Everywhere. It was atrocious but no one ever seemed to do anything about it. Adults called it sibling rivalry and the kids at school were too scared of her."

That, I think as I check my empty cup, was the curse of being a child. The number of adults who told me Denise was just jealous was staggering. Lots of reasons but not enough preventative action.

I start folding my word search sheet, mulling over the black and white memories I have of school. Old, murky and monochrome in nature. Sure, Denise was there, but I don't quite recall Tabitha.

"So what happened then?" I ask, unsure of whether I'm imagining the truth or if it is a genuine memory.

"You stood up to her," Tabitha says, lighting a new spark of passion in her eyes. "I remember it so clearly. A March day like this, in the rain. She'd thrown me down into a puddle and I was crying. Kids were pointing and laughing. Then suddenly you appeared and called a teacher." She looks down at her cup and smiles. "She got into a huff and ran away, and you helped me out of the puddle. You got awarded for it by staff, though they never asked why I was in the puddle to begin with."

They never did. And I remember that award, the only time I ever won one of them weekly tributes to good deeds.

I scoff at the thought.

"Awarding good behaviour that should come naturally."

Tabitha laughs. This time it catches me off guard. I remember now, she deserved her spot on the choir.

"I always thought that," she says. "Anyway, my sister is, um, locked up now."

Oh. My stomach knots a little.

She must see it on my face because she suddenly springs alive.

"No, no, I don't mean in a unit or anything, I mean she's in prison for battery." Tabitha's smile dies, and the room feels less alive with it. "Not that I'm proud or happy about that."

"Oh." I still don't feel any better about that. If anything, I should be singing 'I knew it!' from the top of my lungs and laughing at Denise's poor fortune. Yet, there's not a single urge to be found dwelling in my bones.

If anything, there's a strange emptiness that's creeping up within me. A shadow of disappointment. Not only has Denise remained the same all these years but, it seems, so have I.

"Well, it sounds silly but when I was little you were my hero," Tabitha says. It catches me off guard and my reply sits in my throat.

This can't be right. Surely this is another trick. It's been eight years, I'm sure Denise has moved on. Well, I was sure. And yet, Tabitha is still looking so unsure, and awkward, and polite. I need to grow and stop being wilted by the memories of an adolescent bully.

"When I was at home Denise was the villain of all my games," she says, her cheeks blushing an amazing rosy-hue. "I could never think of how to defeat her until you did. So I wanted to say thank you."

I stare down at my list of dictator names, aptly distracting myself by imagining Denise's name in the cluster of letters. I'm not good at this, I'm not sure what to say, and yet words just roll off my tongue, surprising even myself.

"And you said you wanted to say sorry?" I ask, unaware I'd even remembered that bit and worried I'd made it up until Tabitha nods.

"Yes," she says, banishing that ever-welcome smile again as she does. "I want to say sorry for never returning the favour. For never defeating her back in school. I was always too cowardly, even after seeing you do it so easily. But I remembered what you did, and I feel braver now."

"I didn't do it," I remind her. "She persisted in attacking me for years, and it only stopped because we both finished secondary school."

Almost cutting through my words, Tabitha lights with life again, eager to correct me, and I'm dumbfounded into silence.

"But you persisted too!" she says, almost lunging across the table as she takes my hands. Her warmth shouldn't surprise me but it does, and I pull away. Her eyes don't leave mine. "You could've changed school, or–or given up, but you didn't. In fact, Denise was always moaning about how well you did."

What a lovely bit of light to change an entire perspective of an experience. So powerful, so subtle and so pure in nature that I can't argue it away. I'd never thought of myself as strong, especially after all those times I was dismissed by a teacher.

Tabitha smiles and plays with her scarf.

There's no instruction manual for how to talk about things like this, how to reassure someone they weren't at fault. It isn't easy being a child, much less a frightened one.

I go to speak when something catches my eye. Tabitha's scarf unravelling and loosening around her neck. While it is brief, the fading bruise I see is enough to paint a very detailed picture. A sad, but beautiful picture, guided by the words she just spoke to me, 'For never defeating her back in school.'

"But you've defeated her now, haven't you?" I ask.

Tabitha's eyes lock on mine, wide-eyed and glistening. Her scarf has reassigned its position and she laughs away that little bit of fear I sense creeping up her chest, like it is mine. Such horrors I can imagine.

"We outgrew the playground," Tabitha tells me. "Unfortunately for her, police don't like bullies." She laughs nervously again, and clears her throat. "But thank you. If you hadn't done it then, I wouldn't have had the courage now. It sounds strange." It does, a little. "But if you could do it then, for someone else, a complete stranger, then I could do it now. So, again, thank you."

I smile.

The clamminess in my hands has subsided and the knots in my stomach all but disappeared for butterflies. Despite the topic, I almost wish this conversation didn't have to end.

I stand and stretch, taking my cup as I do.

"Oh, are you going?" she asks. For a moment she seems as disappointed, and the sweat returns in my palms.

In eight years I haven't grown, and I've less bravery than my nine-year-old self. Grow up, Evelyn. Grow up and enjoy this moment with this wonderful woman.

"No," I say, gesturing my cup to her. "Another hot chocolate."

Loose Ends

SAM KAYE

THROUGH THE HEAVY RAIN, JOHN WATCHED THE LITTLE girl jump from one muddy puddle to the next; her parents shouted something that looked like "stop it." She continued nonetheless; her little red wellingtons being used to their fullest. John decided her name was Molly as her smile and curly blonde hair reminded him of his departed niece. It made the job easier sometimes.

He stretched his neck slightly to the left and right, savouring the cool trickle of fresh rain water he allowed to run over him; never taking his eye from the scope.

He had been laying on the roof of the old boxing club in the relentless rain for three hours, thirty-four minutes and sixteen seconds now, cradling his prized British-made AWM sniper rifle. Through his scope he watched tirelessly, waiting.

A young couple came into view, walking and holding hands. The woman, whose face was partly obscured by a scarf, was holding a butterfly umbrella which they both hid under. They weren't talking, just walking by the river, hand in hand. John swallowed and flexed his trigger finger as her head passed the centre of his crosshair; that place was reserved. They passed and left his sights.

His mark, a thirty-two year old male who goes by the name of Peta, had the smallest case file John had ever seen; just a name, several grainy photos and some notes. Whoever had been surveying him made reference to the targets frequent runs through Boundary Park on a Saturday and Thursday afternoon between the hours of fourteen and eighteen hundred. It was perfect hit material.

Setting up in the rain was a risk, but if the target was into his running as much as John hoped, a bit of wet wouldn't stop him.

He gently shook his head, flicking the rain from his fishing hat.

He waited.

A runner came into view, the first since he started watch. John trailed his scope across to the target; the tightening of his obliques burning from the prior hours of stillness. The target runner was obscured, in a black-hooded poncho. *Who runs in a poncho?* John thought as he rested his index finger firmly against the trigger, keeping the target's head within the cross hairs. About six feet tall—*check*, strong posture, flexed knees and head held high, male—*check*, and an experienced runner by his movements. John just couldn't see his face yet; the chase was on.

The target came to a stop and appeared to be gesturing something, from the opposite direction an old female dog-walker approached. The dog was a small, pathetic looking Westie wearing a traditional tartan body-suit. The elderly owner wore an identically coloured bonnet. The target looked up to face the old girl, and John panned across to see her smile. *They know each other,* he thought.

John rolled his shoulders and steadied his aim, keeping a trained eye on the old woman. She dragged her reluctant mutt towards the target, saying something whilst gesturing to the rain. John kept the pressure on the trigger. The target nodded to her.

She spoke as she passed him.

He turned to face her, revealing himself: bearded, button-nosed and wide eyed. Not the target. He jogged on, unaware that his life was, for several moments, in someone else's hands.

John exhaled. The rain grew heavier, as did his eyes. He waited.

A few minutes passed before another man came into view. John's entire body tensed painfully as the face of his mark, Peta, filled his scope. John registered that his target was dressed in a full tailored suit and had red stains on his shirt and was hobbling. *He's injured?* John thought.

John knew better than to hesitate. He scanned the leaves of the trees around the target, watching them dance in the wind and made a slight adjustment to his scope. He took one last look at the target's pained face.

He squeezed the trigger.

The AWM recoiled slightly as the round left the barrel at nine-hundred metres per second. Through his scope, John watched as the target's head jolted to the side; an eight millimetre hole blown through his skull and temporal lobe.

John released the trigger as the target fell to his knees, before falling flat on his face. It only took a second for the puddle of water he'd landed in to become a puddle of blood. The target was motionless, well and truly dead.

John brought himself up to his knees, wasting no time in disassembling the rifle into three smaller pieces, all of which slotted into his custom-made briefcase. He scooped up the additional five-round magazine and spent cartridge from the floor and swapped it for the small mobile phone that he had put in the case to keep dry.

He vacated the roof via the steel stair case at the back of the building, briefcase and phone in hand.

When he reached the side alley between the club and charity shop he switched on the small Nokia, never breaking stride, and dialled the only number he cared to remember. As it rung, he made his way out onto Canon Street and over to his 1983 XR3i Ford Escort. He unlocked the boot and loaded it with the briefcase before quickly running around to the driver's door, getting in and finally escaping the rain. The line connected.

'Case seventeen is closed,' John said.

'Your feedback is appreciated.' The electronic voice was quick and genderless as usual.

The line closed.

John threw the phone on to the passenger seat and rubbed his temples, watching the beads of rain run down the windscreen. The closure of case seventeen would be enough to keep John afloat for a good year or so, if he felt inclined. A drone of sirens broke through the pattering of rain. *Time to move out.* He keyed the ignition but stopped as a new sound invaded his quiet space; his phone. He pensively scooped it from the passenger seat and checked the caller ID which showed "Withheld"—it always was. He didn't expect a call for another week or so and thought about ignoring it, but he knew that someone would visit him again and he didn't want that. He let it ring once more in his hand before answering.

'Bradbury Pest Control, how can I help?' he said.

The line was silent save for an electronic hum. He waited for the coded response.

'Do you deal with field mice?' The female voice sounded chirpy, authentic almost.

'Only if the price is right,' he said, the line changing pitch as authentication was verified.

'Seventy-six, Paines Drive, today.' This time the voice was electronic. The line closed.

They must be desperate, John thought as he stared at the blank Nokia screen. Paines Drive was roughly seven miles away, he'd still be home in good time to drown the day away. He pulled a Mayfair from a crumpled cigarette packet in the glove compartment and lit it, quickly enjoying the long pull of hot smoke before starting the old Ford and driving off into the rain, leaving the sirens and the dead behind him.

The ride to Paines Drive was short and quiet, relentless rain keeping the Sunday drivers and shoppers at bay. The road itself reminded John of the street he grew up on: council houses, boarded-up windows, neglected front gardens used for old white goods and the occasional forty-something smoking a roll-up at their door. Number seventy-six fit the area rather well in that respect, only better kept.

John pulled up outside and surveyed the property for a minute. The plain grass garden had been recently cut, the knee-high bush squarely trimmed and the yellow stained net curtain replaced for a cream one; it looked lived in, drawing no unwanted attention.

John got out of the car and leant against the driver's door. He took a look around—a few parked cars and no one appeared to be paying any attention to him. He unzipped a small pocket on the hip of his combats and carefully pulled out a single silver key and made his way into the house.

John did his part and collected up the takeaway leaflets and local newspapers that had accumulated inside the door and added them to the pile above the gas-meter cupboard. The small detached house was as elaborate as they come, with a fully-furnished open-plan living area complete with sofas, a television and a bookcase. The company made no mistakes when setting up a place like this; it was just another home on the street. He stood and listened, smelling the clean air; he was alone. He wiped his shoes on the mat and headed to the compact kitchen which was fully equipped like any other. John felt like he was intruding in someone's home as the company had even made an effort to leave a glass jar of biscuits beside a red kettle.

Behind the sink, ahead of the small netted window over-looking the garden, John ran his finger along the tiled window frame, looking for the fault line. As he applied pressure, it lifted slightly to reveal a small recess; an envelope hidden within.

'Bingo,' John muttered to himself as he broke the seal of the package which felt much lighter than usual. From it, he pulled a single sheet of paper that was precisely folded. John felt a wave of unease, something didn't feel right. He opened it regardless.

"Thank you for your service." Written in neat blue ink.

A sudden realisation burned through him.

The small window shattered into a million pieces. The kitchen came to life as everything behind John exploded from a blanket of automatic gunfire coming from the small garden. He covered his face as lumps of plaster and glass rained down on him.

'JESUS FUCKING CHRIST!' He crawled across the kitchen floor, still bombarded by the debris. He got up and charged for the door, making a swift exit whilst fumbling for his car keys. It took three attempts to ram the key into the door; he quickly realised why central locking was so popular. He threw himself in and fired up the old Ford but before he could even put her into gear his driver side window exploded across his face; bullets peppering the dash board. He slammed his foot on the accelerator and wheel-spun as the tyres fought to find grip of the wet road.

But it was in vain.

The gunman sprayed a carpet of gunfire across the back of the car, bursting the passenger side tyre. John quickly wrestled the wheel to bring back control but couldn't stop the car from spinning around to face the house he had just escaped. He threw the car into reverse but was immediately incapacitated as three bullets ploughed through his left shoulder and bicep. He screamed in agony and tried to open the door, everything inside him telling him to run.

MICHAEL KEPT HIS RIFLE TRAINED ON HIS TARGET WHO was clearly injured. The old Ford XR3i would have been a nice prize but he hadn't expected his target to make it as far as he did. He marched to within a metre of the bonnet and aimed at the man's face. This man, who's case file was one of the smallest Michael had ever seen, didn't look scared, sad or angry. He seemed to accept the situation, knowing his fight was over. Michael pulled the trigger, and watched the targets head jolt back violently; skull and brain-matter blending nicely into the brown leather headrest. Michael heard a nearby woman scream and the clatter of opening doors and windows. He slid the compact rifle into his oversized trench coat and jogged swiftly into the alleyway opposite, leading to Pickering Street where his black BMW awaited. He unlocked it using the keyfob and opened the boot, lifted the carpet and slotted the rifle into the space where a spare wheel formerly lived. He slipped into the black leather driver's seat and pulled out his

Nokia, dialling the only number he needed to remember.

'Case fifteen is closed,' he said.

'Your feedback is appreciated.' The electronic voice was quick and genderless. The line closed.

Before Michael pocketed his phone, it rang in his hand. The caller ID showed "Withheld" as usual. He answered.

'Princes Pest Control, how can I help?'

'Do you deal with field mice?'

The Old Man

GHILLIE

His eyes, old and narrowed, look out across the rolling sea. Eyes that had seen the swell of the water as his ship ploughed through the waves and across oceans. Eyes that now are seeing the changing face of the world. A body that had felt the freezing cold of Scottish winters and hands that used to be strong enough to grip hold of life.

Fingers with no dexterity and legs too weak to walk, the result of old age and tired old bones. Sitting in his wheelchair on the promenade, he looks out over the churning foam huddled in a warm jacket against the icy cold wind; thinking of how, not so long ago, he as a child was running across those sands. A life so rich and filled with happiness. He, like so many before him, never thought that his world would change; never thought that it would be like this when he became old. In his mind he is still a boy but with the experience and knowledge of a man.

He still wants to do so much, to achieve so much, and still has the ability and the desire to learn. He thinks of all the things which he has gained; all the different skills which he had spent a lifetime perfecting. And now he has no use for them, although they would be forever engraved upon his memory. Skills and knowledge which had motivated him and shaped his life; now redundant. Only the slimmest of possibilities that those skills may be useful to someone, but nobody is really that interested. People have their own lives and worries; different priorities and different sets of values.

His love of the great outdoors is crucial to his feeling of well-being. Breathing in fresh sea air, he seems not to care if it is accompanied by rain or sleet. He, deep in thought, thinks of his favourite season, autumn; when green leaves turn to brown, red and gold before the cold dark days of winter, after which the first watery rays of sunshine appear, heralding the beginning of a new spring. Nature's regeneration.

His face is pitted and lined by advancing years; his cheeks sallow. Hardened by weather but still so full of character. He doesn't mind the rain. When it rains nobody can see that the man is quietly sobbing.

Stray

SEB REILLY

THE SKY GLOWED RED FROM THE FOREST FIRE AND THE hills echoed with the barks of wild dogs.

Elvio sat on the step of a stranger's house, shuffling his deck of cards. The sun was barely up and the town still asleep but he was ready for the day's graft. In this early peace he could finally relax. He liked the feel of the cards as they flickered through his fingers, the burst of air on his hands cooler than the breeze coming over the sea.

He walked down the hill at a slow pace, wary of his ankle. It still ached. He took a moment to rest and admired the view: villas set into the steep rock, surrounded by banana plants and olive groves; the shimmer of the sea in the grey morning light. It almost took the thought of the dogs away.

At the harbour Elvio drank from the water fountain and washed his face and hands. It was meant for tourists but even at high season there was plenty to go around. He liked to get to the waterfront early and reserve the best place for his hustle. He could still pass for thirteen, even though he was much older, and tourists loved the idea of a local boy beating them at cards. It was his smile and charm that they bought, not the tricks.

He set up on the pavement near the beach, by the busiest footpath. Just like every morning he ran through his repertoire while the streets were empty, practicing his jokes in English, French, Dutch and German. Locals knew his game so he had to learn new languages for the visitors.

Once he was ready he laid out his first hand and waited for the tourists to arrive.

A boat was leaving the marina and the restaurants were preparing for the day, but it was all background and in the breeze Elvio barely heard them. It was a gentle hum of quiet that he enjoyed as if it was the first time.

A tapping across the street broke through Elvio's calm. Paws on the pavement. He looked up, hoping it was a cat but knowing it was not.

The dog stopped, ears alert and tail straight. It stared at him, eye to eye, like it remembered. He knew that dog.

Elvio didn't move. He was back in the forest, trees casting spindle shadows in the moonlight, as the dog stood over him, its slobber dripping on his neck, feet on his chest, teeth bared and rumbling as it growled, hot stinking breath suffocating him. It was hungry then and it was hungry now.

One hand out to steady him, the other on the floor, Elvio crouched. His ankle stabbed with pain. He stood, slowly, ready to fight or run. The dog tensed, its tongue hanging low and flecked in dry spittle.

The coach appeared without warning as the hillside had blocked the sound of its engine. The dog looked up, ears back, and watched it approach. As it stopped there was a whining squeal that could have been its brakes or the dog, Elvio couldn't tell. The dog glared at Elvio, barked, and walked out of sight. The coach doors opened and tourists filled the street.

Elvio sat down, breathing fast. His pulse beat loudly on his jaw. He swallowed air, desperate to fill his tightening lungs. He was running through the forest, the jaws of the dog scything at his back, growls and barks filling the night as the pack rounded on him. The moon sunk behind a cloud and the fog rose and he was blind in the darkness, leaping to avoid branches and clumps of fern, dogs pacing him either side and their leader howling in his wake. He forced a swallow and the throbbing in his ankle hit him.

'Are you all right?'

An elderly woman was leaning over him, baseball cap and designer anorak. Elvio adjusted his position to ease the pain and smiled at her, his heart calming.

'Yes, thank you. Bad leg.'

'Oh, you poor thing.' She turned to an old man dragging luggage. 'Harold, look at this poor boy.' She smiled at Elvio. 'Are you from here? We need a guide.'

Elvio was about to speak, working through his answer to make sure his English sounded good, when the old man interrupted.

'No dear, the hotel will sort all that. Come on, he's probably a homeless.'

'But Harold, his leg?'

'We need to check in.' The old man rolled the suitcase away.

'Sorry, dear.' The old woman took out her purse. 'Here, take this.' She passed him a ten Euro note.

'Thank you, madam.' He bowed his head and smiled graciously. 'Very kind. Have nice stay in hotel.'

She tilted her head like a lizard in the sun and smiled warmly at him, then scurried away to catch up with her baggage.

The rest of the tourists avoided Elvio, as his exchange with the old woman had made him look like a beggar. He could have made three times what she gave him, but then again, he might have made nothing. He waited for them to disperse and the coach to leave, then eyed the street for the dog, but it was gone.

Elvio decided to move to a different spot in case he'd been reported to the hotel staff. There were some young lovers on the beach but their clothes were next to them so he wouldn't be able to steal a different shirt without being noticed. He hoped the new tourists wouldn't remember his face.

He settled on a bench near the café on the other side of the hotel, near the beach. The strip was still practically empty, but the early risers were already eating breakfast on the hotel balcony.

A shadow loomed over the bench as Elvio laid out his cards. An older grifter, all stubble and muscle, was leering at him. His eyes were like the dog's.

'*Ei, garoto*,' he said. 'Hey, kid. There's a tax to sit there. *Imposto. Vinte Euro.* Twenty.'

'*Desculpe.* Sorry, I'll go.'

'*Não.*' The grifter shook his head and made a fist. 'Pay, you've sat now. *Você paga.*'

Elvio pulled the old woman's ten Euro note from his waistband. 'I only have this. *Aqui está.*'

'*Bem.*' The grifter snatched it. 'Now you owe me another twenty. *Vinte. Taxa de reembolso.*'

The grifter grinned and walked away, lighting a cigarette and looking for other traders to rip off. Elvio hadn't seen him before; he must be new. Although Elvio didn't want to pay, it was better than not paying. Maybe he could dodge the other twenty if the Polícia picked up the grifter later, when the tourists were out. Perhaps not.

The morning was warming up and Elvio couldn't get comfortable. Panic stirred under his skin. He felt trapped, halfway up a tree after scrambling to escape the dogs, watching them circle and bark beneath him, dark shapes twisting through the midnight fog.

He picked up his cards and tried to shuffle them but his thumbs wouldn't work. The sky above the hills inland was a brighter red than before; the fire must be spreading. There were no sirens, but the wind was heading inland so the sound wouldn't make it this way. The tourists would notice the glow soon.

Elvio's stomach ached almost as much as his ankle, but it was a fast pain that came on quickly. How long since he last ate? He couldn't remember. No time for that now, he needed to make at least fifty Euro in the next few hours. Bus tickets weren't cheap.

A few tourists appeared, walking out of the hotel. The old woman from before was there, followed by the old man. He was talking to two Policiais. He pointed at Elvio. The Policiais nodded and separated, walking towards him across the esplanade. They must have reported him for begging, and the Polícia didn't like beggars.

Elvio scraped up his cards from the bench, shaving skin from his knuckle, and ran as fast as his ankle would allow him. Stabbing pain almost crippled his first step but he ran still, crossing the road before an oncoming car. The Policiais were close but they had to wait for the car, its irate horn screaming after Elvio. He charged up the drystone steps into the banana plantation that climbed the steep hill, the Policiais following. He was nimble and darted between the bananeiras, ducking under the cachos of bananas and skipping over the hoses strewn to irrigate the cliff soil. He clambered like an animal on all fours until he was sure the Policiais had given up, and then ascended further.

He reached a road. If the Policiais decided to pursue him they would be in a car, so he crossed quickly. The asphalt jarred his leg and his ankle burned and thudded but he had to ignore it. His hand was bleeding and his arms covered with scratches and cuts from the arbustos. He ran up more drystone steps and into another plantation, pushing on and up until he was out of sight of the road and sheltered from view.

It took Elvio a while to calm his breathing and his heart was kicking the inside of his chest as if it wanted to escape.

He considered this could be the worst day of his life, and then he heard the growling. It was low and throaty and he knew it.

The dog from earlier, the one from the night before, was stood a way behind him, teeth bared. As he turned his head it saw his eyes and barked a single, terrifying snap, and charged.

Elvio ran.

He ran through the plantation, through an olive grove, under grapevines, past avocado trees, across a road, through gardens and up slopes, across pátios and verandas, always climbing, always up, always towards the forest. The sky was darker here, the clouds that gathered around the hilltops a deep, smoky red from the fires.

Every time Elvio looked back the dog was there, snarling and drooling as it pounded after him. Others were following, the pack growing larger than he had seen before. The fire must have driven them from the trees and into the town. Their eyes were vengeance, their muscles steel and their blood ice. Their bellies were hungry for flesh and they followed.

Still he ran and the dogs chased.

The air grew thick with fog and moisture and steam and it was hot and Elvio could see fire engines and lights and Bombeiros with hoses spraying the trees but still he ran. The dogs barked and growled and whipped at his legs and the fire grew closer and he reached the trees but still he ran. The ground became warm and the air heavy with smoke and his skin pricked with sweat and his ankle throbbed but still he ran.

The fire was taller than a house; a burning wall across the forest, wider than the hill. It scorched the ground and roared and trees cracked and snapped and Elvio could hear nothing else. He stopped as a reflex, forgetting the dogs, the sea of flame before him.

He had only wanted to scare the dogs, to create a distraction. Look what his box of matches had become. In the tree he lit the box and dropped it in a dry scrub. It was to clear the dogs. He jumped and landed badly on his ankle, escaping downhill as the flames spread. It was enough to get away from the pack. By the time he reached the town the sun was rising. It was the first, and would be the last time he slept in the forest. Now the forest was alive with fire. It burned.

Over the crashing flames Elvio heard a bark. He turned. Behind him, the dogs had lined up. All of them, hundreds, staring at him, around that one dog, the leader. He had strayed into their territory, taken their home. He had started the fire that reflected in their eyes. He understood them then, and he was calm.

'*Sinto muito*,' he said. 'I am sorry.'

The sky glowed red from the forest fire and the hills echoed with the barks of wild dogs.

Misjudged

STEPHANIE UPTON

Susan took another sip from her glass; it tasted good, so she allowed another mouthful to slide down her throat. These work parties were all the same, but at least the music wasn't too loud this time. Her eyes checked across the room, Stewart was laughing raucously at some joke or another, she guessed it was rude, he always loved crude jokes. Her back rested against the wall; she knew Stewart worked hard at being popular; he said people were useful commodities. She took another drink, and as she gazed into the crowd, she noticed a young girl staring vehemently at Stewart. The girl's eyes seemed to slant, her face had a tight expression, yet her body seemed to be trembling. Susan looked at her intently; she was sure she was right, that girl hated Stewart. The last drop of wine trickled into Susan's mouth, it was time to get some more, but as she moved away, the girl stayed in her mind.

"Hello," greeted Alice. "Lovely to see you again Mrs. Jones."

Susan looked at the false face that had spoken, did she have to reply? She knew she had to; it was all an acting game.

"Alice, how are you?" she asked, not really wanting an answer. Stewart's last little fling was of no importance to her. Well, that wasn't exactly true, since Alice had disappeared Stewart had been more demanding in the bedroom, and his violent sexual activities were horrendously painful.

"I'm fine," Alice said with a fixed smile. "The party's great, isn't it?"

"Yes dear, just fabulous," Susan replied. "It's good of you to have your 'leaving do' in your own home."

"I'm loving seeing everyone this happy, work can be very stressful, you know."

"I'm sure it can," Susan said politely as the ex-lover moved away.

Thankful the small-talk was over, Susan put a double vodka in her glass. It was great to be able to drink, Stewart didn't allow her to have alcohol in the house, so social gatherings were the only chance she had to release her unhappiness. She downed the vodka and took a gin. The table with the crisps looked inviting; she wasn't allowed to eat fatty foods, Stewart said her rations had to remain strict, being hungry was part of life. Apparently, because she was middle-aged, she needed to work at staying a size 10. She reached and took a handful.

"Stewart's a great bloke," Ted said as he stood next to her. "He's such a laugh to work with, and he's good with the clients."

"Indeed, I'm a lucky woman," she said as she took another swig of liquor. She had to play the grateful wife; he'd punish her if she didn't praise him enough.

"He's just helped a woman with Multiple Sclerosis to get a place at 'The Angel.' None of us thought it would be possible. Such a terrific bloke."

"He certainly knows how to get what he wants," she said as she took a handful of peanuts and stuck them uncouthly into her mouth.

"He's such a decent guy. I wouldn't have got my job without his assistance."

Susan knew Stewart's own self-interest always lay behind his altruistic gestures. "I expect you've been a great help to him," she said while chewing like a starved animal. Food felt such a pleasure; she took some more.

Ted watched her with a look of disgust on his face. "I've been helping him with his latest project," he said, glancing away as she swallowed loudly.

"What project's that?" She could hear her words were starting to slur, but she didn't care. Suddenly, she held onto the table, her stomach cramps from where Stewart had thumped her were becoming aggressive again. Why hadn't she vacuumed the bedroom? She'd thought it didn't need it, but she should've known he'd notice.

"Rehousing girls from the women's refuge."

Susan squirmed as her insides rolled.

"That's one of our clients over there," he said flicking his head in the direction of the young girl who she'd noticed earlier. "Have you had too much to drink?" he asked as she clung heavily onto the edge of the table.

"I guess so," she replied, not wanting to give away her secret. She straightened up and finished her glass. She needed more alcohol to take away her pain. She looked over at the drinks counter; it seemed to be signalling to her, like some long-lost friend.

"What job do you do?" the ignorant man continued as he scanned her shabby attire.

She wished she did work, but Stewart wouldn't allow it. She hated not having any money of her own, answering to Stewart, as he checked every receipt it was always a nerve-racking experience.

"I'm just a housewife," she said apologetically. Stewart was right; no one would want to employ her; she was unable to survive without him. "My glass is empty," she added, "I'll just go and top it up."

Ted bowed his head, and she guessed he was relieved the conversation was over.

She winced as her wrong-sized shoes rubbed against her blistered feet, but Stewart had bought them in the sale, so they were a bargain. Then as she staggered past a group of people, she overheard someone say, "That's his wife, she's always drunk at these events. Stewart's a saint with her." There was no point in answering, she couldn't explain, and they wouldn't believe her anyway. Above the sound of the alcohol pouring into her welcoming glass, she heard Stewart's boisterous laugh emanating from the other room. She peered around the door; she could see him standing there in his designer clothes and properly sized shoes, he looked quite the gentleman. He seemed busily engrossed with a group of women; that's good, she thought, she was free for a while longer, and she took another drink.

Her bladder felt full, so she wobbled her way towards the stairs. It felt a long climb, her stomach was aching, and her feet were killing her. She pulled herself up by the banister, the pressure easing as her arms took the weight from her hurting body.

"I'm Daisy," said a quiet voice behind her. "Can I help you, you seem a little worse for wares?"

Susan turned to face the girl from the women's refuge. How she envied her; she could escape, while she was too old to run away.

"Just had too much of the old drink," Susan replied through gritted teeth. "Are you enjoying the party?" she added as she reached the landing.

"Not really. Stewart said I had to come. I'm supposed to be telling everyone how grateful I am that he got my mother a place at The Angel."

"That was your mother?"

The girl dropped her voice as she grabbed the rail at the top of the stairs. "I wanted to say sorry to you, and I thought you should know that..." She looked at the floor and whispered, "I didn't want to do it, but he made me...with him and his mate."

"What! Together?"

"He told me he'd rather let Mum rot. There was nothing anyone could do for her, but if I wanted his help, then he'd put himself out...if I'd go the extra mile."

"Who was the other man? Did they hurt you?"

"Someone he knew from another department." The girl's eyes filled with tears. "It was horrible, he..."

"Susan, hurry up," shouted Stewart from the hallway. "The new Managing Director's just arrived." He glared from the bottom of the stairs. "Daisy, you come down and meet him too."

"We need the toilet; we'll be down in a bit," Susan shouted as she turned back towards the bathroom. It was too late, she could hear him charging up the stairs.

"Come on Daisy," he yelled as he pulled the girl's arm. "You can tell him how great I am."

Susan watched as the girl yanked her arm away. Stewart twisted and lost his balance. It all seemed to happen in slow motion, his legs went from under him, and he fell head first down the stairs. He lay motionless at the bottom.

The girl screamed as Susan ran down after him.

"Someone call an ambulance," she bellowed as she stood over his unresponsive body.

"You, drunken idiot, get out of my way," yelled a woman who knelt to check his pulse. "He's alive," she yelled to everyone who had gathered round.

The ambulance men came and seemed concerned about Stewart's back. "It might be broken," one of them explained to Susan.

Ted whispered to her, "Such a terrible thing to happen to such a lovely man. I'll organise a collection for him. And if he needs twenty-four-hour care, I'll help you."

"I'm divorcing him," she replied without flinching a muscle. "I want a life." Her eyes held his. "And my advice to you is to keep your money, and leave him...to rot."

"How could you be so self-centred?"

"And how could you be so stupid?"

The Year the Flamingos Came

MAGGIE HARRIS

THE SUMMER THE FLAMINGOS CAME KERRY RODE THE bus, the child inside her curled tight like a whelk. It was 1975. Pegwell Bay came into sight: the Hoverport. A chorus arose, women out of their seats, skin and cotton, nylon, tweed, shoulders.

'Bleeding heck!'

'What are they, storks or summat?'

'Herons, ain't they?'

'They're never herons! They's flaming flamingos they is! We sawr them when we took our lot to Florida last year. Remember I brought in the photos?'

Cars had pulled in by the Viking Ship, and people were getting out. Their driver slowed down and Kerry pressed her nose against the glass. Flamingos they certainly were. A flock of some two dozen neon ballerinas, incongruous on the mudflats. Beyond them the Channel hovered, still and grey. Beside them, a hovercraft waiting, and two figures digging bait.

Kerry felt her heart leap as she watched them. Home birds. They were home birds. Around her the women were still flaffing. The child inside her flipped as if in response, a light ripple.

'Do you think they got beached like that poor whale last year?'

'I dunno! Maybe they got blown in with the wind or something!'

'There weren't no wind last night! News said we're in for a long hot summer!'

Their faces steamed the glass. The flamingos became hazy and disappeared as the bus cruised out into the slow-moving traffic. They slipped out of Kerry's vision.

Around her the factory flock settled down, apart from Beth, who took the opportunity to light up, settling her reed-thin hips against the back of her seat, continuing the tale of awe with her neighbour. The thin wisp of smoke curled away from her conductor's hand, mimicking the tail of a kite in a robust wind.

'Well, you never bleeding know, you never bleeding know, do ya? I tell you it's a sign that; mark my words.'

'They was bold as brass weren't they? Not that I know nuttin 'bout birds but them lot wasn't them that come every year was they?'

'No, they ain't. Hey! You don't reckon they escaped from a zoo or something, do you? Or that circus? They was putting up posters at the Lord of the Manor...'

'Them kind o' birds don't do tricks you dumb twit!'

'Oo you calling dumb Irene? You didn't even know what they called, you was calling them herons!'

Laughter bounced off the seats like party balloons, each ear catching its sound, magnifying it, carrying it forwards and backwards, soaring on a ripple of words.

Kerry looked across through the window on the land side. The towers of the power station loomed upwards, grey and austere, tucked in at the waist, matronly bell-like shapes. Behind them the country was flat and uninteresting, the squat fireworks outbuildings an echo broken by the barest glimpse of the ruined walls of Richborough Fort. Someone had told her it had been there since the Romans. The bus was approaching the factories, and the turgid smell from the polluted sea entered, replacing the air of jollity with its insidious presence. Beth ground her cigarette out into the ashtray on the arm of the seat, and the rustling of bags replaced the chatter, the spread of breeze-block and corrugated buildings coming into view, the bus slowing down, pulling into the concrete yard.

THE BATHING HAT SLIPPED BENEATH HER FINGERS, THE wheel slicing it neatly. She sighed. She was never going to get the hang of this. Around her strips of decimated rubber decorated her workbench. The noise from the machines filled the workshop, hummed and rattled; women's fingers flew, heads bowed, words and brief bursts of laughter breaking through Radio 2 on the loudspeaker. The DJ, Terry Wogan, joked about it only being 200 shopping days to Christmas.

The smell of sulphur snaked in from the back, the men shifting trays of rubber into a cavern of heat. All day long banter cut and thrust between them and the women on the shop-floor. The taste of rubber clung to their tongues. The heat influenced the way they moved in their overalls, unbuttoned to the waist. Cigarettes hung from their lips by the open hangar door. Waves of cool air ushered in constant moans of complaint.

'Shut that bleeding door!'

'Bit o' fresh air, put hair on yer chest, you lot!'

'Whadda you know Frank? You ain't got neither!'

'More belly than chest, that one!'

'You should bleeding stay 'ome you lot, get yer husband's tea on time!'

The girl next to her had mastered it already. A neat pile of swimming hats lay in her tray. The supervisor had come round, and had looked down at Kerry's massacred strips with thin, pursed lips.

She got up to go to the loo, feeling the supervisor's eyes on her. Five minutes, she mouthed.

Two of the women from the bus were smoking over the sink. They glanced swiftly over at Kerry and carried on their conversation.

She went in and sat on the loo. She didn't even want a wee. She just wanted to sit for a minute out of the clatter and hum. She felt useless. Now she was pregnant she was going to be even more useless. She'd been on hot water bottles all through her trial period here. She didn't know why they moved her to swim-hats. Maybe the season had something to do with it.

Words winged their way over the toilet cubicle. 'They're taking on another bunch of new ones next week.'

'Chrissake, another six months and they'll be threatening redundancies again. Did you see the news last night about the pits? Blighters weren't happy with closin' down Chislet; first excuse was no more steam trains, now they're going on about steel. Happen there won't be no call fer it one day.'

'That'll never happen. That can't happen. You can't take away work like that from men. And they'll always need coal, folk'll always need coal.'

'Well the way they was talking it didn't sound too good. Don't know what my Jim would do if he ever lost his job.'

'Shouldn't worry about it love. Anyroad, we'd better go before that jumped-up chargehand has something to say.'

BACK AT HER BENCH, KERRY PICKED UP ANOTHER TWO sections of semi-circular rubber.

Beth glanced over at her. 'How you getting on ducks?'

Kerry met her eyes sheepishly. 'I'm not really.'

She looked enviously over at Beth's bench. Scores of neatly beaded swim-hats sat waiting for collection. Curved like slices of watermelon, a rainbow stack of lemons and lilacs. Beth's hands sped round the wheel, perfect hats fell into her basket. Kerry had a moment of déjà vu but it wouldn't reveal itself to her.

Beth's hands stilled for a moment and she beckoned her over. ''Ere. Come and watch me for a minute.'

Kerry slid off her seat and walked round the bench.

Beth held up the two offending pieces of rubber. 'First thing ducks, think: think of the money. Think how much extra in that little brown envelope on a Thursday for every thousand of these. Next, think: plonkers. Who'd wear shit like this? Not me, you wouldn't even get me in no chlorine pool. Ramsgate beach under a sunshade, that'll do. So think of them heads like Humpty Dumpty and stick 'em together. These two pieces here, they're sweethearts, see? They want to be together, sweet and close as a seam. Take your time, slide it, feed it with both fingers like if you're knitting, fingers working together then Zip! There you are. If you're no good at this, they'll have you doing French letters and you won't like that. Never hear the end of it!'

Kerry giggled, then put her hand to her mouth as Beth was as serious as a Preacher on Good Friday. She didn't let on she knew nothing about knitting.

At lunchtime she went into the canteen for a cuppa, unfolding her sandwiches at one of the Formica tables. Sue from hot water bottles joined her.

'Hiya Kerry, how you doing in swimming hats?'

Sue was tiny, with a sleek head of black hair that swung above her shoulders.

Kerry sighed. 'Not very good. Dunno why they moved me. I was getting on fine in bottles.'

'Orders I suppose. They do it all the time, you can't get too comfy. You'll get the hang of it, don't worry.'

'They were talking redundancies in the loo…'

'They do that all the time! Gossipy old bags!'

Kerry laughed.

'You gotta remember…oh but you won't know this not coming from round here…the wimmin 'ere ain't long been earning good money. Most, like me mum, come off the land, picking spuds and cabbages and apples in all weathers. These here wages are bloody good money, 'specially if you can top it up with extra. Some even take plugs 'ome to assemble, sit in front the telly, click click bloody click. But the bloody men still holding out their bleeding hands come Thursday payday! Tell you what though, I ain't sticking round here long if I can help it, I'm gonna get a nice clean job working in Chelsea Girl or somewhere like that.'

THEY DOWNED TOOLS SHARP AT 4.45. TEN MINUTES TO tidy up, do time sheets, visit the loo. At 4.55 they put coats on, made their way to the double doors. At 5 the siren went, trilling through the factory. Doors swung open all along the concrete walkway, women emerging from workshop doors gabbling and joining the throng, heading to the buses. Kerry thought of it as the Avenue of the Farmyard, it reminded her of her grandmother's geese, her father's cows.

The Saturday past, one of the girls had got married. On the Friday, her workmates dressed her up in strips of rubber for a wedding gown, complete with train, weighed her down with Durex condoms ringed with plastic flowers, adorning her head like a veil, and made her walk down the yard, the laughter and well-wishers all breaking out of the workshop doors. The comments were ribald and coarse, and Kerry had felt shame for the girl. There was no way she would ever sacrifice herself so.

She'd forgotten about the flamingos. As the bus slowed down through Cliffsend, she noticed the cars lining the side of the road, the crowds and the cameras. Hand-held cameras took their place alongside those on tripods. They were filming the flamingos, pinning their elegance down on the mudflats.

SHE TURNED THE KEY TO HER FLAT, HER FINGERS SORE from practising on the wheel all day. A letter lay on the door mat. The familiar stamp brought a smile to her face. But the worry lurched inside her, reminding her. She read it at the dining table, drinking tea. The first part of her mother's letters were always full of warnings. She mustn't wear her skirts too short or forget where she came from. She must eat enough greens. She must be careful not to make friends with people before she knew them. Most of all she must stay away from those English boys, they thought foreign girls were easy pickings. Had she found a congregation yet? She thanked her for the small money order she'd sent, hoped she was getting to grips with her job at the bank. Everybody at home was so proud of her. They were hoping her sister Evangeline would be able to join her soon.

She folded the letter back into the envelope and sat looking out onto the communal courtyard. The people in the flat above had left their rubbish at the side of the bin again. But she couldn't complain, look what she had had to do to get this place.

The flamingos were on the Southern News. An expert said it was highly unusual that flamingos would migrate this far. Most likely they were blown off course, or perhaps the predicted warm weather blew them here. No one knew how long they would stay. Perhaps they were just resting.

Before she went to sleep Kerry remembered what Beth's hands, spinning over the wheel, reminded her of. It was a storybook image: Rumpelstiltskin, spinning straw into gold, and the princess standing before him afraid, commanded to do the same.

Her sister Evangeline's face swum before her as she fell asleep. When she dreamed, Rumpelstiltskin came into the room. He wore the face of her landlord.

Looking for Robert

ROGER JEFFERIES

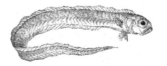

I was in Thailand; it was the first week in February, about six weeks after the tsunami. It was hot and humid. The heat exhausted me. There was debris everywhere, collapsed buildings, uprooted palm trees, and a rancid, earthy, wet smell. Temporary mortuaries were full of bodies piled on makeshift metal shelving. There were noticeboards where photographs and sad appeals hung damply and people wandered listlessly between them; I was one of them. I met some forensic teams who were trying to match evidence to human remains. The ones I saw laid out were purple, swollen, torn and twisted.

Looking at the corpses and the crowds relentlessly searching I understood that a body could not be laid to rest until it was matched to a name. Otherwise there were names and no bodies, names which might end up like those on the war memorials in Flanders, list upon list carefully engraved, the sole relics of lives lost.

A French doctor whom I met said that the whole place seemed to him like purgatory.

"What do you mean?"

"These are people waiting to be released into 'eaven. They are being cleansed and punished at the same time. They cannot go until their family find them and bury them and release them. Lost souls until then."

I didn't understand the separation of souls from bodies. I don't think I believe in an afterlife. But the idea that this foetid place was just a waiting room was somehow right.

I WAS LOOKING FOR MY BROTHER ROBERT. THERE WAS no sign of him. I visited several hospitals where the wounded lay. But he wasn't being treated. If his body still lay stacked in a store no one had got round to pulling it out for identification. And I had nothing to give the doctors to help.

I was hugely irritated by the fruitless trip and with Robert for disappearing, and with my mother for making me go.

After the Christmas holidays in 2004 he had failed to return to his accountants' practice. As he had never married he had named me as the next of kin in the firm's records, rather than Mother, and I was phoned and asked if I had any information. The firm had no idea where he had intended to spend Christmas. Of course, I had none either. They wondered if he could have been caught up in the tsunami disaster.

For some years I had had no communication with him at all. We were estranged and it went a long way back. Mother had done her best with us. Dad was killed in a road accident when I was six. Robert was four years older and angry about it.

He didn't come to terms with it, and when Mother married Reg, quite quickly afterwards, a much older man, Robert's alienation became fixed. He hated Reg, and despised Mother, especially when it became clear that she had been seeing him before Dad died. Nothing would soften him.

In fact Reg was a rich man and I got on well enough with him; he was devoted to Mother. When I left home long after Robert, he and Mother moved to a distant part of Lincolnshire, into a seventeenth century manor, Fossdyke House. Then about nine months before the disappearance, Reg died, leaving Mother wrapped in grief and isolated in the big house. Reg's children from his first marriage were now disputing his will which more or less cut them out but left Mother a wealthy woman. All this I heard about in weekly tearful phone calls, so when Robert went missing she was distraught and insisted we find him, or rather that I find him.

"I know he's been horrid to me and you have nothing to do with him, but I can't bear the thought of him in that terrible place. If he's dead we must bury him properly and I won't take no for an answer. Reg would have said the same."

"But we don't know he's anywhere near there, Mother. You're jumping to conclusions"

"Find out. Isn't there a help line? Make an effort, Jack."

I WAS TEACHING AT A SMALL PRIMARY SCHOOL; IT WAS AN enclosed world, a womb; its little routines and rituals contained me. I didn't want to step outside it. But in the end I got some time off to make the enquiries.

I actually started in his flat. It was difficult to find a key, and I was deeply reluctant to rummage. When we were boys he'd forcibly kept me out of his room. I kept thinking he would walk in and be furious.

There were no brochures in the flat; his bank wouldn't tell me about his account. I didn't know who his friends were. I couldn't find an address book, and his computer was password protected.

Mother was right about the help line however. Eventually someone, the police I think, got hold of passenger lists on airlines. Her instinct was right too. Robert had gone to Phuket, the place where immense waves had smashed across the beaches and splintered everything, tossing bodies into death. He may have been caught up in it.

"You must go at once," Mother cried over the phone. "Get compassionate leave."

"Why would I do that?"

"Blood's thicker than water."

"I've never believed that; Robert's living proof it isn't."

That's how I got to Thailand.

WHEN I GOT BACK MOTHER WAS DISTRESSED; SHE HAD hoped I would find him alive. Now we had to assume that he was dead and we would have to identify his body if it was lying in some mortuary. We were asked for his finger prints and to describe any physical peculiarities. The worst thing was his dental records because we couldn't find his dentist. The bank eventually found a payment to one in Robert's account.

The months went by. Robert's records didn't match any of the unidentified European bodies. It was a nightmare; everything was in limbo, his flat, his job, his money, his mortgage. I really didn't want to have to go back to Thailand. In the end he was recorded as missing, believed drowned. But the Thai authorities wouldn't give us a death certificate on that basis.

Mother was depressed, ill with it. She had the dispute with Reg's children to deal with and now Robert's likely death. It was too much, I think. In July she was found dead in bed at Fossdyke House. It was a great shock to me, far greater than Robert's drowning. The doctor said it was stress. Remembering the French doctor, I wondered if she would join the souls seeking entry to the after-life in which I didn't believe. No sooner had we buried her in the delightful nearby church than it became apparent that nothing much could be done about her own will.

ROBERT AND A SOLICITOR WERE THE EXECUTORS, BUT not me. Given Robert's treatment of her I couldn't understand that, but I suppose it said something about her lack of confidence in me. Most of her money was the inheritance from Reg which was still frozen pending the legal challenge by Reg's children. She had left her money equally between Robert and me but if Robert died without children before her, it was all to come to me. Robert wasn't officially dead so her will was frozen too. Only if it could all be unfrozen could I get my inheritance, a comfortably large amount. The solicitor and I agreed we should start by getting a declaration that Robert was officially dead.

I was told that after seven years there was a presumption of death when someone was missing, but we could try and persuade a court before that. The lawyers thought it would be a struggle so soon, but that we had a case.

Reg's children were tired of being fobbed off. Taking advantage of the situation they sued. The solicitor as Mother's executor had to deal with it. At the same time we were applying to the court to have Robert declared dead. The papers picked up the whole story. Headlines such as, 'The Tsunami casts a long shadow,' and 'The poor primary teacher who wants the lot,' over pictures of me and Mother. It was written up as a lurid family saga; they found everything out about us, and even Reg's former wife. Somehow they made us look greedy and argumentative. And I was photographed leaving the school gates.

Uninhabited Fossdyke House was a problem. It was remote. It was beautiful and listed, but because of the frozen wills we were not allowed to sell it. We had to make sure it was looked after and I went up from time to time. Mother and Reg had chosen to live there because it was a long way away and they could be alone. Reg did a good job in bringing it up to date, and the indoor pool was terrific.

I didn't like staying in it by myself as a matter of fact. It was handsome enough as a house. It was not grand, just solid and very pleasant to look at. But alone in the place I found it impossible to relax. It was noisy, the building creaked. The trees were constantly shaken and pushed by the wind; outside, the rustling leaves made a noise like the sea. And I had to resist the fears of the night, solitary and without neighbours.

After our bad publicity in the papers it was time again for me to get up to Lincolnshire for a caretaker visit. I was fully expecting the press to be camped outside Fossdyke House. But it's a long way even for them. It was the end of October.

The gardener from the village had put the heating on; although the pool was normally kept drained he had also refilled it. There were logs for the open fires and some food in the fridge.

I switched on a lot of lights; I felt more comfortable like that. Reg had put in a sound system and I could have music wherever I went. I wasn't in the mood for a swim. Any useful place was miles away, including a pub. For some people it would be a wonderful place to escape to, to hide.

I went to bed early; I lay there listening to the sounds of the house and the trees beyond the window. Then I let go and slipped into sleep.

I woke up in the middle of the night. I thought there had been a knock on the door. As I stirred, there it was again. Had the gardener come into the house? But it was black, darkness as only the countryside without a moon can lay down. I was still half asleep. I found the lights; I called out.

I went to the door and opened it slightly; in the distance I thought I could see a faint glow, beyond the landing down below. Outside the bedroom I turned on the lights as I went downstairs. I felt slightly better, but I could hear sounds coming from the direction of the swimming pool.

The pool was down a short corridor in a barn like structure at the back of the house, tastefully done of course. I opened the door, the overhead lights were switched on. Someone was swimming vigorously towards the other end. It was a man, and what at first I took to be a swimming cap was a bald head. He turned and saw me. He lay back in the water with his head and shoulders on the edge of the pool, his legs floating in front of him.

"Who the hell are you?" I shouted.

"A good question, little Jack."

I knew the voice, but he was almost unrecognisable. "Robert?"

He called back, "Once I was. It's Halloween. Had you forgotten? This is my trick and your treat. I took advantage of the wave to disappear. In the world out there I'm no-one, no-trace. I've never had so much fun, but I thought I'd come and collect my inheritance, all of it. You'll have to divi up, Jack, and I'll push off again into nowhere."

I sat down abruptly where I was. Was I properly awake, was it a dream? It was appalling. He was alive and we were asking for him to be declared dead.

He called across the pool, "You'll be able to sell the story."

"It killed Mother."

"You wouldn't expect me to care."

"You broke in."

"Not difficult."

I have never thought of myself as a violent man but I could usually beat Robert when we fought, and I boxed at school. But I knew with absolute clarity I would kill him now. No one knew where he was. He was missing, about to be presumed dead. He was a non-person. And I wasn't going to share my inheritance with him. Now I would put him to rest; send him onwards out of purgatory where he had been wandering. He would be really dead, with all souls.

It was easier to do than I could have imagined. I ran fast down the poolside and jumped in. I fought him; he was taken completely by surprise. He didn't expect it of me. I got him under water and he drowned properly this time.

I buried him among the far trees, very carefully and deep. I let the water out of the pool. And I returned the bicycle he'd hired in some bogus name.

Robert was declared dead by the court, which of course he was, though not quite as believed, and I bought off Reg's children. I stopped teaching, and, when the money was in the bank, I went to live in Fossdyke House.

I keep an eye on Robert. There's a lot of undergrowth now.

The Second Floor

DAVID CHITTY

A MAN GRABS ME FROM THE WAITING ROOM AND TAKES me through a bare corridor. He coughs, hacking up a trail of spittle that lingers in his rust coloured beard. He doesn't make any effort to get rid of it, just wipes his hands on his stained, grey suit. He ushers me into a small office.

A woman looks up from behind her desk. "Thanks, Karen."

The man, Karen, waves a hand at the woman, mumbling something under his breath as he walks away.

"Come in and take a seat, Alex," she says, pointing at a row of chairs.

I take the second in the line. The plaque on her desk reads 'Simon'. Weird names for people in this place.

Simon gathers a few papers from her desk and attaches them to a clipboard. She turns in her chair and looks at me. "Do you know why you've been called in today?"

"No idea."

She puts on a pair of glasses, flips through her papers and removes them, keeping them in her hand and looks at me. "There have been some concerns raised about your conduct."

"What kinds of concerns?"

Simon looks through the papers again. The room's remarkably stark; I expected something different. Grey walls, dull furniture and everything's bare. The only personal touch is a photo of Simon's pet snake on her desk. I hope it's her pet, anyway.

"Seventeen women have presented their accounts of the sexual harassment that you've been directing at them."

How did she find out about that? I start to say something but Simon holds up her hands and stops me.

"I'm not here to debate or argue about this, Alex. All I'm doing is telling you what we've been told. You have a meeting scheduled on the second floor when you're done here with me."

"Who am I seeing, and why?"

"You'll find that out when you get there."

"Is there nothing I can say in my defence?" Might as well try something.

"We're past that stage now, Alex."

Simon pushes herself to her feet, drops her glasses and her clipboard onto the desk and motions for me to follow. She walks ahead, the clinking of her heels echoing throughout the room. She opens a door that leads to a long, empty corridor. I follow behind her.

When we reach the end, Simon presses the button to call the lift. The doors slide open and she holds her arm in the gap.

"Head up to the second floor," Simon says. Her tone gives me the impression that she's not asking me; she's ordering me.

I step inside, Simon withdraws her hand and I press the '2' on the wall. The doors close and the lift starts moving.

Within moments the lift grinds to a halt and the doors shudder open. I step out. It's an empty concert hall. It looks like it hasn't been touched in a couple of years; cobwebs hang between the rows of chairs; dust cakes everything else. A woman sits on the stage, a spotlight raining down on her. I walk towards her, each step kicking up a cloud of dust.

She doesn't move until I reach the stage. Then the woman stands and points at the front row. I take a seat.

"Betty again, not that you need to be told. You know who I am." Betty starts pacing the stage, throwing her hands in the air with every word she shouts. "You know what I'm talking about. You know what it all means. You were there, and it was great. Great."

I have no idea what she's going on about.

"We were all there when it happened. The great fire of 2017, the fire that claimed the lives of nineteen billion souls. A burn that was felt throughout the world. Everyone knew it and everyone knew that I would be the one to save you all. Betty can save everyone. It'll be great again."

What the hell is she talking about?

"It's going to be good again, you see. France and the leprechauns will be united once again, and they'll be proven to be the greatest friends in the history of ever. It'll be glorious. Fabulous even. It'll be so good that Santa himself will rejoice."

What is this? Do I have to stay here? Is this my appointment? To sit here and listen to some random woman named Betty rambling on? To see her spout nothing but nonsense and blow hot air? She's still going on. I think she mentioned something about a stegosaurus marching on Downing Street. I'm done. I can't do this anymore. This can't be right.

I stand up in a cloud of dust. Betty doesn't stop. The further I get away from her, the louder she gets. She's practically screaming at me as I make it back to the lift. The door opens almost instantly after I press the button. I get in and I'm enclosed without pressing a thing. There isn't a button for the ground floor, and I keep slamming the first floor but we're not moving. I start to press all the buttons, slamming them with the palm of my hand. The light for the ninth floor finally comes on and the lift starts chugging.

With every second in the lift the temperature plummets. I'm beginning to think I should have stayed where I was. The lights shut off and the doors open an inch, letting an icy wind through the small gap. I get my fingers into the gap and pry the doors open the rest of the way.

The wind hits me with its full force now. My vision adjusts to the darkness and I can see what's beyond the doors. I should have stayed up on the second floor.

It's a lake of ice. There are people protruding, half stuck, some buried completely. I step forward. The bodies around me are all locking their gaze on me. No part of them moves, other than their eyes. I keep going. The cavern around me doesn't seem to have an end. Neither does the frozen lake under me. The wind gets stronger the further I go. I must be getting closer to the source of it.

I really should have stayed on the second floor.

Standing at the edge of a precipice, there isn't anything that could have prepared me for this. Something is sticking out of the ice. Whatever it is, it's trapped in the frozen lake at the waist. Its torso is bigger than a bus, six leathery wings frantically slap the air, spreading the icy wind throughout whatever this place is. It has three faces, each of them gnawing on a human inside. The thing looks up and notices me. There's a sadness in all six of its eyes as it locks gaze with me. It looks to the left of me.

"You really should have stayed where you belong." Simon steps up to the edge of the crevice and looks down at the creature below. "There's an order. We can't let this betrayal slide, unfortunately." She sighs and pulls her phone out of her pocket. "I need to pull soul number 7-8-1-3-2-5-8-6-2-0-1 and pull them from Ring Two to Nine." Simon listens to the response, turns away from me and starts walking away. "And get the fucking renovations on the Ninth Circle sorted out already! We can't have Satan sitting down here scaring the stiffs anymore. Sort it out."

Paint Me

CONNOR SANSBY

THERE'S SOMETHING MAGICAL ABOUT BREAKING INTO a gallery at night. I don't like crowds, but I love art, so over the years I've discovered the best time to visit a gallery is at night.

This isn't a story about breaking into a gallery, it's a story about what happens after breaking in.

This night I'd been in the gallery for all of three minutes, perfectly alone while the night watchmen take their nap in the security rooms when I began to hear scuffling.

The gallery was empty, but sure enough behind the wall, in one of the exhibition rooms, there was the distinct sound of someone moving.

Naturally, this piqued my interest. Was there another late night intruder pondering the works, or was it just the sound of the building, wires and fans buzzing? I decided to explore and made my way around to the source of the noise.

When a gallery brings in a new exhibition, it's not uncommon to close off a room while the preparation is taking place. This seemed to be the case, judging by the tarpaulin hung over the entrance archway, affixed with masking tape.

I peeled back the tape and slid through the narrow opening as the sheet swung away from the wall.

The room was filled with paintings, created by masters in centuries past, lining the three sides of the room, but, in the centre was the marquee attraction, the one work they hoped would draw the crowds.

Covered in white cloth, leaving only the podium and plaque free from obstruction, I had to see what the fuss would be about.

I crept my way along the exhibition, focused in on this target, and reaching out a tentative hand I grabbed the sheet and pulled with a flourish, the magician's reveal.

Under the crude covering had been a statue of a woman of transfixing beauty. I averted my gaze for the briefest of moments, to the bronze plaque affixed to the pedestal, hoping for some name.

'A vision in white marble.' Truth in advertising, ladies and gentleman.

I once more met her solid gaze, and began to give her the once over, slowly circling the figure, admiring the handiwork, the fortitude and talent to have created something so perfect.

It wasn't until the third pass round I noticed the one blemish. Across the left arm, outstretched with dainty fingers, someone had smeared paint, a rainbow colour burst across the forearm of the figure.

I reached out, to check if the paint was wet, a recent work of vandalism, a tragedy of transport, or maybe an intrinsic statement on the design.

I was millimetres from feeling the paint when the statue gasped, and her other hand darted to protect the paint.

"Don't, it isn't yours."

I was stunned, not that the statue was talking to me, but rather to hear another voice in the still of the museum, and I stumbled out an apology, "I'm sorry, it's just out of place."

Me and the statue began to converse, I asked her what the paint was, and she explained to me, hurriedly, like a guilty child, that it was her artwork.

She had added the colour to herself, to define part of her identity.

"A statue, is the host to someone else's message," she offered me, "but, I don't get to decide what I say."

"But why paint on yourself?" I was beginning to grasp the absurdity of the moment, engaging a marble statue in conversation.

"It's the only place people would notice it, I have no other canvas."

"Paint me." The words fell out of my mouth before I could analyse what I was saying.

She hesitated, for the briefest of instances, before producing a fine paintbrush.

The tip was already wet, and dutifully I rolled up my sleeve, presenting my arm as her new canvas.

Slowly, the fibres moved against my skin, each stroke gentle but with purpose, elegantly curving across the surface. By the time she had finished, she had covered most of the visible skin in an assortment of colours. It occurred to me she had never changed paint brushes or dipped into any reservoir of pigment.

I turned the arm back towards myself, excited to see what had been crafted across me.

Against the backdrop of a rising sun, the words "Thank you, please stay."

I looked at the window, and surely enough I saw the sun begin to peer over the horizon, in the distance.

I had to leave sometime soon, but I found that as I thought about turning and running to the bathrooms to hide while the gallery opened, I was instead climbing aboard the pedestal, curling around her feet, like a cat at the fireplace. Her skin was not so cold, and I began to close my eyes. I knew where I was needed and so I stayed.

The Child's Story

CHARLES DICKENS

ONCE UPON A TIME, A GOOD MANY YEARS AGO, THERE was a traveller, and he set out upon a journey. It was a magic journey, and was to seem very long when he began it, and very short when he got half way through.

He travelled along a rather dark path for some little time, without meeting anything, until at last he came to a beautiful child. So he said to the child, "What do you do here?" And the child said, "I am always at play. Come and play with me!"

So, he played with that child, the whole day long, and they were very merry. The sky was so blue, the sun was so bright, the water was so sparkling, the leaves were so green, the flowers were so lovely, and they heard such singing-birds and saw so many butteries, that everything was beautiful. This was in fine weather. When it rained, they loved to watch the falling drops, and to smell the fresh scents. When it blew, it was delightful to listen to the wind, and fancy what it said, as it came rushing from its home—where was that, they wondered!—whistling and howling, driving the clouds before it, bending the trees, rumbling in the chimneys, shaking the house, and making the sea roar in fury. But, when it snowed, that was best of all; for, they liked nothing so well as to look up at the white flakes falling fast and thick, like down from the breasts of millions of white birds; and to see how smooth and deep the drift was; and to listen to the hush upon the paths and roads.

They had plenty of the finest toys in the world, and the most astonishing picture-books: all about scimitars and slippers and turbans, and dwarfs and giants and genii and fairies, and blue-beards and bean-stalks and riches and caverns and forests and Valentines and Orsons: and all new and all true.

But, one day, of a sudden, the traveller lost the child. He called to him over and over again, but got no answer. So, he went upon his road, and went on for a little while without meeting anything, until at last he came to a handsome boy. So, he said to the boy, "What do you do here?" And the boy said, "I am always learning. Come and learn with me."

So he learned with that boy about Jupiter and Juno, and the Greeks and the Romans, and I don't know what, and learned more than I could tell—or he either, for he soon forgot a great deal of it. But, they were not always learning; they had the merriest games that ever were played. They rowed upon the river in summer, and skated on the ice in winter; they were active afoot, and active on horseback; at cricket, and all games at ball; at prisoner's base, hare and hounds, follow my leader, and more sports than I can think of; nobody could beat them. They had holidays too, and Twelfth cakes, and parties where they danced till midnight, and real Theatres where they saw palaces of real gold and silver rise out of the real earth, and saw all the wonders of the world at once. As to friends, they had such dear friends and so many of them, that I want the time to reckon them up. They were all young, like the handsome boy, and were never to be strange to one another all their lives through.

Still, one day, in the midst of all these pleasures, the traveller lost the boy as he had lost the child, and, after calling to him in vain, went on upon his journey. So he went on for a little while without seeing anything, until at last he came to a young man. So, he said to the young man, "What do you do here?" And the young man said, "I am always in love. Come and love with me."

So, he went away with that young man, and presently they came to one of the prettiest girls that ever was seen—just like Fanny in the corner there—and she had eyes like Fanny, and hair like Fanny, and dimples like Fanny's, and she laughed and coloured just as Fanny does while I am talking about her. So, the young man fell in love directly—just as Somebody I won't mention, the first time he came here, did with Fanny. Well! he was teased sometimes—just as Somebody used to be by Fanny; and they quarrelled sometimes—just as Somebody and Fanny used to quarrel; and they made it up, and sat in the dark, and wrote letters every day, and never were happy asunder, and were always looking out for one another and pretending not to, and were engaged at Christmas-time, and sat close to one another by the fire, and were going to be married very soon— all exactly like Somebody I won't mention, and Fanny!

But, the traveller lost them one day, as he had lost the rest of his friends, and, after calling to them to come back, which they never did, went on upon his journey. So, he went on for a little while without seeing anything, until at last he came to a middle-aged gentleman. So, he said to the gentleman, "What are you doing here?" And his answer was, "I am always busy. Come and be busy with me!"

So, he began to be very busy with that gentleman, and they went on through the wood together. The whole journey was through a wood, only it had been open and green at first, like a wood in spring; and now began to be thick and dark, like a wood in summer; some of the little trees that had come out earliest, were even turning brown. The gentleman was not alone, but had a lady of about the same age with him, who was his Wife; and they had children, who were with them too. So, they all went on together through the wood, cutting down the trees, and making a path through the branches and the fallen leaves, and carrying burdens, and working hard.

Sometimes, they came to a long green avenue that opened into deeper woods. Then they would hear a very little, distant voice crying, "Father, father, I am another child! Stop for me!" And presently they would see a very little figure, growing larger as it came along, running to join them. When it came up, they all crowded round it, and kissed and welcomed it; and then they all went on together.

Sometimes, they came to several avenues at once, and then they all stood still, and one of the children said, "Father, I am going to sea," and another said, "Father, I am going to India," and another, "Father, I am going to seek my fortune where I can," and another, "Father, I am going to Heaven!" So, with many tears at parting, they went, solitary, down those avenues, each child upon its way; and the child who went to Heaven, rose into the golden air and vanished.

Whenever these partings happened, the traveller looked at the gentleman, and saw him glance up at the sky above the trees, where the day was beginning to decline, and the sunset to come on. He saw, too, that his hair was turning grey. But, they never could rest long, for they had their journey to perform, and it was necessary for them to be always busy.

At last, there had been so many partings that there were no children left, and only the traveller, the gentleman, and the lady, went upon their way in company. And now the wood was yellow; and now brown; and the leaves, even of the forest trees, began to fall.

So, they came to an avenue that was darker than the rest, and were pressing forward on their journey without looking down it when the lady stopped.

"My husband," said the lady. "I am called."

They listened, and they heard a voice a long way down the avenue, say, "Mother, mother!"

It was the voice of the first child who had said, "I am going to Heaven!" and the father said, "I pray not yet. The sunset is very near. I pray not yet!"

But, the voice cried, "Mother, mother!" without minding him, though his hair was now quite white, and tears were on his face.

Then, the mother, who was already drawn into the shade of the dark avenue and moving away with her arms still round his neck, kissed him, and said, "My dearest, I am summoned, and I go!" And she was gone. And the traveller and he were left alone together.

And they went on and on together, until they came to very near the end of the wood: so near, that they could see the sunset shining red before them through the trees.

Yet, once more, while he broke his way among the branches, the traveller lost his friend. He called and called, but there was no reply, and when he passed out of the wood, and saw the peaceful sun going down upon a wide purple prospect, he came to an old man sitting on a fallen tree. So, he said to the old man, "What do you do here?" And the old man said with a calm smile, "I am always remembering. Come and remember with me!"

So the traveller sat down by the side of that old man, face to face with the serene sunset; and all his friends came softly back and stood around him. The beautiful child, the handsome boy, the young man in love, the father, mother, and children: every one of them was there, and he had lost nothing. So, he loved them all, and was kind and forbearing with them all, and was always pleased to watch them all, and they all honoured and loved him. And I think the traveller must be yourself, dear Grandfather, because this what you do to us, and what we do to you.

All the Postcards Never Sent

ROSIE ESCOTT

HE WROTE THE POSTCARD WITHOUT THINKING VERY much. It said, "Mary, now I am away from you, I know I want to be with you when I am home. I am on one knee and I am asking you to be my wife. Tell me your answer when I come home. Love always, Derek."

He posted it into the yellow post box and went into the cafe. He had a stiff drink and it was then that he started to think about love. Was his love good enough for her? Would he be the best husband? He was no good at catching spiders, he knew that. No…he was no good with spiders. It simply would not do.

He went back to the post box and waited. When the postman came, he gesticulated wildly until the postcard was safely back in his pocket and he went back to the cheap hotel alone. He kept the card in his bag and carried it across France, Italy, Greece and all the way home, where he watched Mary marry Bernard. He helped Bernard choose the ring. He was the best man, but Bernard was better; he was good with spiders. Mary had four children.

DEREK FRAMED THE POSTCARD AND KEPT IT ON HIS mantelpiece; his trophy of loss, of all the letters never sent. When Mary died she smiled and thought only of Derek. When Mary died he posted the postcard.

The Face

JOHN MOUNT

NIGEL VOID HATED HIS FACE FROM THE DAY IT BETRAYED him. Every morning he cast a mistrustful glance at the mirror then dragged a safety razor across cheeks that bore the faint shadow of teenage blemishes that countless facials and laser treatments hadn't entirely eradicated. Back then his face had been puckish, full of damaged adolescent beauty. The acne had only underscored the conviction of leading theatre critics that his raw, youthful performances had an intensity that stood comparison with the company of angry young icons of the Sixties that included Albert Finney, Richard Harris and Stanley Baker.

As he matured into a powerhouse of the stage his face healed but its lunar surface added an extra dimension to his performance. He simply had more physical texture to play with than his contemporaries and something primal about his facial expression and body language was picked up in the stage lighting and communicated all the way to the back row of the house. Here was a Hamlet or a Richard III whose emotions genuinely ripped across his face. When he made the inevitable transition to cinema he had to dial down his playing a few notches and his complexion became a long-term work in progress for Hollywood's most trusted dermatologists.

Now though that celebrated theatrical countenance, whose individual pores he'd learned to expand and contract at will, grew rebellious, insolent even. He'd first noticed the change in transit—stepping in and out of limousines, moving through airport lounges, negotiating restaurant receptions and checking in at hotel lobbies. The people who took care of the small but essential day-to-day chores and had once made the practicalities of life glide effortlessly before him: chauffeurs, porters, receptionists, dental hygienists, barmen and waiters, now appeared to be somehow more hesitant, less confident in their response to him.

At first it seemed perfectly rational to him that his ever-increasing legend went before him and the sheer force of his charisma overwhelmed them, then, less confidently, he decided it was simply the result of falling standards in the service industry. When that explanation no longer satisfied him he decided to study these people he'd previously taken for granted more closely and found that they were looking at him differently because they were uncertain how to react. They couldn't read his face. A discovery that would horrify any actor.

Void started glancing at reflective surfaces whenever this happened and discovered that faint, elusive expressions were now wont to flicker across his face. After the uncertainty and ambiguity came caprice. Now he started making inappropriate facial expressions, not lewd or provocative, not at first anyway, his face simply no longer matched his feelings, thoughts or intentions. He knew straightaway that he had to work harder at controlling his communications before he started to gain a reputation for being eccentric and unpredictable.

Somehow he kept this all tightly contained when he was working but his agent, Vivian Slice, was the first to notice something was up and asked him straight what was going on. Void let it all out but had to repeat himself several times to Vivian because of his unreliable facial mannerisms.

"Not to worry love," Vivian soothed. "We can get you that therapist who worked wonders on Harold after his stroke. We can minimise this. But I'm going to get you a new assistant who'll keep you safe from harm's way. And we're going to have to choreograph personal appearances very carefully from now on."

Void was somewhat comforted now that he'd taken Vivian into his confidence but he found the rigors of his new daily routine daunting and tedious. They had a couple of wobbles on his next two films but nothing too disastrous and they wisely kept well away from the stage. It was far too risky trying to control himself night after night before a live audience. The stress was undoubtedly taking its toll on him and he seemed to age noticeably overnight. Despite the best efforts of his dresser and make-up artist comments were made by showbiz columnists, especially in the run up to his latest movie.

And here he was sitting in his trailer fretting about his next session in front of the camera. He'd been on set early this morning and nailed his first three takes with ease. Hart X, the young director everyone wanted to work since his Càmera D'Or at Cannes last summer, had been thrilled with his performance and despite their many differences in temperament, taste and technique they seemed to be forming an agreeable working relationship quite quickly.

Wim, Void's new general factotum, glided silently into the trailer and placed a nutritionally balanced salad and a carafe of mineral water on the table, then melted into the shadows. Void thanked him and picked at his plate. Wim had been a good choice, discreet, unflappable, androgynous, slight yet as had been shown a number of times now extraordinarily strong and able to anticipate his employer's next move before his face had time to misbehave. Wim had already saved Void from considerable embarrassment during several high-profile engagements. You hardly knew he was there until a persuasive command or a firm hand on a sleeve moved a troublesome reporter or a pushy producer away from Void's presence or swiftly conveyed him from a film festival stage or TV studio to his hotel suite. A cashmere security blanket, that's what Wim provided and it was allowing Nigel Void to come and go on set as he pleased, safe in his head and safe from unwanted complications.

Wim rematerialised at the sound of intercoms outside the trailer and before one of the runners could knock on the door it was open and he was summoning Void on set for the next sequence. Hart X was keen on shadows and ambiguity and was making the most of the budget to incorporate some expensive night shooting into the picture. All to the good as far as Void and Slice were concerned—a low profile on and off set was just the thing these days. There was a flurry of activity around Void as he took his place on the sound stage, Wim ensured all went smoothly; Vivian had insisted that none of the production staff were to meet Void's gaze throughout shooting. Fortunately, this was deemed an entirely reasonable request by the standards of today's over-pampered male leads and flouncing divas. Hair and make-up withdrew silently as lighting and cameras took over.

"Ok but quicker," barked the 1st assistant director.

"Carpe noctem," murmured Hart X.

Void did some neat little bits of business with a coffee cup and aced his first line. He didn't need his co-star for this, in fact he'd made sure he matched eye-lines with her but kept two-shots down to a minimum.

The old Void liked to know his leading ladies. He'd ask them impertinent questions, encourage them, use them to enhance his screen performance and give the film some zest, he'd even married two of them but now he couldn't trust himself. And his co-star was potentially the one fly in the ointment. Mistral Thane was ushered in by her entourage and beckoned Hart from his chair.

"I've had some new thoughts on this scene," she said, "and I'm sure the character's intuitions are guiding me."

Void's eyes glazed over like a dead mackerel's on a fish-monger's slab but somewhat worryingly, the corners of his mouth briefly turned in opposite directions. "Don't be distracted," said a voice in his head. He glanced back and saw Wim retreating silently.

"Good," purred Hart, "just let the script speak to you."

The first take went well. Void moved towards Mistral with beguiling intensity, their characters were just about to realize their physical attraction and act upon it.

"I'm not feeling these words Hart," she said. "Would my character really be attracted to Nigel at this moment?"

"I believe she would, but you must convince me," he replied.

Void knew all too well what this was about, he'd side-stepped attempts to upstage him by the very best talent in Hollywood. Mistral had ruled the catwalks at Paris and Milan from an extraordinarily young age and had made the transition to acting after brief flirtations with rock music and photography. She'd taken advice from some of the shrewdest names in fashion and the art world but still felt she lacked authority and tried to buy it through acting classes, humanitarian causes and psychoanalysis. And here she was doing a two shot with a grand thespian, the genuine article.

Void could have told her that all she had to do was let the camera rest on her cheekbones and trust in her strong physical presence. She had a clear, memorable voice so the words could be left to take care of themselves. After ten takes it was clear that this was not going to happen anytime soon. Apparently it was not enough for her to succeed, Nigel Void would have to wilt a little on screen also.

To his credit, Hart X saw what was happening and like any director worth his salt knew that his mind games were the only ones that could be indulged on set. He ordered a couple of slight changes to camera position and lighting, took Void on one side and told him they'd get the take they needed in the next half hour or work around Mistral's performance in the editing suite.

On take 23 Mistral leaned forward, lifted her chin then tilted away from Void at the last second. "Nigel you're not at ease with this either, I can tell, your face isn't quite on the page."

Void measured his breath and drew from a deep well of professional composure. "Oh dearest girl, I just try to find my key light and say my lines without tripping over my teeth. You're playing this perfectly, you look divine and you are smart enough to figure out motivations for both of us and make this scene work."

Take 24 went without a hitch and Hart called for a 45 minute break. Void wondered on the way to his trailer if perhaps he'd been a little too generous or in some obscure sense capitulated to her. When they returned an emboldened Mistral was keen to speed things up and Hart made up for lost time in the schedule. At 2am they were close to wrapping for the night and shot the parting glances as Void and Thane's characters nuzzled fleetingly and went their separate ways.

Out of the corner of his eye Void saw Dominic, the young 3rd assistant director, perched half way up a zip-up tower. He'd been sent on a pointless chore after he'd finally blown up and thrown down his clapperboard in response to repeated sniping from one of the supporting actors about him end-boarding takes too slowly. The boy's face was contorted with rage. He'll be bounced off the film if he doesn't calm down soon thought Void. Continuing his gaze around the set he noticed all the tics, tremors and gestural anomalies of the rest of the crew and the cast. Only Wim retained a mask of impassive calm. Void brightened. He realized that barely one of them could control themselves, not to the same degree that he had mastered, he felt reassured and nodded to Hart that the next take should proceed. Soon he'd be back in his hotel suite sleeping soundly between freshly laundered Swiss cotton bedsheets.

Mistral gazed deeply at Nigel as their shoulders grazed and he hesitated imperceptibly. Wim advanced a full pace behind him as Nigel's attention was caught by a stray eyelash on Mistral's cheek. His tongue shot out, trapped the eyelash then he bit her forcefully on the cheek. Wim had Void's head in his hands before anyone drew breath. He quietly commanded Nigel to relax his jaws and retract his teeth while Mistral screamed and howled and shook in terror. After a few interminable seconds, Void ran his cuff over his bloodied mouth, collapsed into Wim's arms and was carried from the set.

Two ambulance helicopters blinked and clattered across a glittering Californian night sky as Mistral and Void were whisked away to separate exclusive medical centres. Wim had taken the precaution of snatching a long webbing strap from a flight case, wrapping it around Void's face and clipping it securely with a lock.

Void mumbled through uncontrollable sobs. "So near, so near. What's happening to me? The critics' choice, look at me now with my face muzzled like a fifth-rate forgery of Tony Hopkins playing Hannibal Lecter."

Three weeks later Vivian Slice paid a visit to a discreet, stratospherically expensive sanatorium in Malibu. Swaddled in a dark, opulent dressing gown, Nigel Void sat semi-reclined on a bright yellow upholstered lounger facing out across meticulously tended gardens in a secluded canyon that ran down to the sea.

"I can see you've regained your equilibrium," Vivian said. "I have excellent news for you Milor, your loyal servant has been very busy on your behalf and all is well. Frankly your stock is simply soaring. We put your awkward turn down to an allergic reaction to botox serum in Madam's make-up and the merest hint of a lawsuit brought everyone round to our side."

Void nodded, lost in his own thoughts.

"Hart has a shot list that'll keep him busy with the second unit for another two weeks, by which time your consultant has told me you'll be fit to return to set for six more days of shooting and all will be done." Wim shot a quizical look at Void as he took a deep breath.

"I'm taking a long sabbatical after we're finished but with a little help from the hypnosis sessions and the vitamin shots I do seem to be holding up, how's Mistral been?"

Vivian chuckled. "You've done her an immense favour, she finally feels she's a full-blooded actress and one of extraordinary power, she's already planning her wardrobe for the awards season and can't wait to get back on set."

"So be it," Void replied.

Spontaneous applause broke out as Void and Thane appeared on set and took their positions. A full medical crew was on standby, Hart X was smiling benignly and Void could sense that Wim was close by. As the first take was marked he was pleased to see Dominic had held on to his job. That boy was going to be his lucky talisman for the rest of the film, all the omens were good. The scene played without a hitch, there was now a genuine spark between the leads, Hart nodded gently, satisfied that he'd got what he wanted. Void had moved perfectly, in complete control, he'd never been better.

A justified pride coursed through him as he took two paces away from Mistral then turned back to say his final line, his face a picture of poised, sophisticated nonchalance. His nostrils flared slightly as he took a breath before his line: "Let's take my car and shake off LA." Instead his eyes met Mistral's as he murmured tenderly in his cut glass mid-Atlantic baritone: "Schwuiiip, ruargfahrt, blurta, funnuck cark!"

Chisel

REBECCA DELPHINE

DANNY TAKES ONE LAST DRAG OF HIS CIGARETTE BEFORE flicking it onto the grass. He grabs my hands and pulls me up, exhaling the last of the smoke into my face.

"Sorry," he grins, with absolutely no remorse. He knows I'm trying to quit.

My sister Harry walks ahead of us, side by side with Danny's friend Charles. Harry keeps sneaking sideways glimpses of him. She's always worn her heart on her sleeve, but I've never seen her look at anyone like this before. Charles is handsome, in a commercial, teeth-glint-when-he-smiles sort of way. But he's too neat; his uniform is always immaculate, and every strand of his hair seems to be in just the right place. Danny, however, looks like he could have slept in his un-tucked shirt.

For the last seven years, Harry's and my home was Wellington House boarding school, but it got closed down last term. We wanted to spend our final year at a local public school, but Roland, Mother's husband, disagreed. He says children get their best education in boarding schools, and because Mother thinks Roland shits roses, she listened. Six weeks ago they sent us here, to The Hemingway School for Girls. It's just like

Wellington, another listed mansion filled with pretentious brats who believe their parents love them. It makes me sick.

Danny's fingers come under my chin and tilt my face up to his.

"Where are you, Rosie?" His devilish smile rises higher on one side than the other.

Fortunately, Hemingway has a partner school, The Latford School for Boys, and it's right next door. Harry and I have been meeting Danny and Charles three times a week since we arrived. We're on lunch and they're supposed to be playing hockey, but they're never even in their kit.

Shame.

"I was thinking about my mother," I answer.

"She doesn't visit much?"

"Never."

"Ouch," he says.

The boys sports teacher is staring at us, watching us walk along the edge of the field. But he won't do anything. He never does.

Latford's head teacher struts across the field, through the boys playing hockey. They are all distracted by him, passing the ball in slow motion. The Head reaches the sports teacher, and as they chat he glances at us. I hold my breath and wait for him to shout, but he looks away.

I give Danny a bewildered expression.

"We have an arrangement," Danny says. "And besides, it's their last day."

"Both of them are leaving?"

"Retiring," he corrects.

Neither of the men look anywhere near retirement age, but I can tell Danny's not going to elaborate.

"So, do your family visit much?" I nudge into his shoulder. A silver pendant falls out over his loosely fastened tie. It looks like two spirals side by side.

"There's no-one left." He tucks the pendant back under his shirt collar. "I outgrew them."

I roll my eyes. Danny's one of those guys who thinks he's more intelligent than everyone else, above and better. But I like that.

"Don't worry about your parents," Charles tells Harry. "You have me now,"

She must have told him about our crappy parental figures. At Wellington House, while the other girls were away every summer playing happy families, Harry and I were the only ones left.

The sun glints off a silver chain at the back of Charles' neck, just below his pristine hairline. Maybe it's a pendant like Danny's, a sort of boy's club thing they do in their school.

A whistle blows behind us. I look over my shoulder and see the boys on the field collecting up equipment. The sports teacher helps them, but the Head is standing in place, watching us.

We've reached the rusted gates of the old church. Danny said our schools were built around it, but over time funds and religion fell short, and it's been left derelict. Apparently it's haunted, but that sort of thing doesn't bother me. I think it's where boys from Latford take girls from Hemingway to be alone. Harry and I have been playing hard-to-get up until now, but we've finally agreed to go on 'the tour'.

The large gates are chained shut and plastered with 'keep out' signage, but Charles pulls a key from his pocket and unlocks the padlock. He swings the gate open for Harry to step inside. She does, smiling at him, obviously impressed. We all follow. Then Danny takes my hand and leads me to the right, away from them.

"We'll go in round the side," he says.

Charles doesn't bother hiding his smirk.

Danny guides me around the edge of the church, his hand on my back, burning hot through my blouse. We walk up a raised path towards a small door leading into the first floor of the church. A long line of statues accompany the path, covered in moss and white blotches. But they're not the angelic forms I had expected. They cower, slight and childlike. Most of their faces are covered by their hands, and the few whose faces aren't covered have crumbled off completely. The statues closer to the door look newer, like someone started to clean them but gave up just a few statues in.

"Harrowing, aren't they?" Danny whispers. It makes me jump.

"Yes." I rub my hands up and down my arms, over newly appeared goose-bumps.

"Come here." Danny lifts his arm over my shoulders and pulls me into him, still walking me forward. I glue my eyes to the door ahead.

It's just an old church.

He takes out a key and unlocks the door. I prepare to take in a dusty, stale breath, and step inside. Danny follows and shuts the door behind us.

Locks it.

We're on a landing, standing on a clean red carpet. The air is clean too. Candlelight flickers from shelves around us and floats up the stairs from the floor below. I can hear Charles talking from somewhere down there.

"Don't worry about them, they can wait."

I hadn't noticed how close Danny is, his hot breath sweeping down my cheek, onto my throat. I grab a handful of his shirt and pull him even closer. His mouth comes down onto mine and I slowly tug at his bottom lip with my teeth. A gratifying moan escapes him. He lifts me up and I wrap my legs around his waist. I'm lifted onto the ledge of a boarded window. One of my hands is behind his head, running my fingers through his dark, messy hair. My other hand slides along the surface of the thin window, trying to keep balance.

No dust.

His lips move onto my jaw, my neck. I pull off his pointless tie and unbutton his shirt. Both of his hands are under my skirt.

A scream emanates from the floor below.

I pull away, hitting the back of my head against the window pane.

"What was that?"

Danny looks at me through narrowed eyes.

Silence.

He pushes his lips hard against mine.

Then I hear it again, louder.

Harry is screaming.

I shove Danny away and jump off the ledge. I follow her screams down the stairs, yanking my skirt back down.

What is Charles doing to her?

My heart pounds hard against my chest and my blood thuds in my ears. I reach the bottom and glance back at Danny. He's still standing on the landing, topless and pissed off.

How can he not hear her?

I run past rows of pews and through a door. A group of figures stand with their backs to me. I barge my way through to see Harry cowering beneath a man in a suit. It's the head teacher of Latford. He opens his mouth wide, stretching the skin, distorting it, like a snake dislocating its jaw.

I lunge forward with no clue what I'm going to do. I'm grabbed by two boys in Latford blazers. I search along them, along the line of men and boys all staring at Harry and the Head, eagerly awaiting a show.

Bright blue light escapes from the Head's pit of a mouth and pours towards Harry. She scuttles backwards, but the light jumps onto her face and forms a hand. Its fingers pry at her lips, opening her mouth.

All I can do is watch as the light invades her. It pulsates inside her body, illuminating her skin and veins, and flows back into the Head's open mouth. He brings his arms out wide, letting the last of the light explode through his limbs.

Harry doesn't move, or collapse, or cry out with pain. Her wide eyes are open, her screaming mouth stuck in place. She has turned grey.

Tears pour from my eyes and blaze down my cheeks.

"Thank you for your contribution," the Head says.

His voice is younger than it should be. Then I see he is young, a boy of around twelve in an oversized suit. His once greying hair is curly and bronze, his wrinkles gone, his life rejuvenated.

Stolen from my sister.

"Chisel?" he asks the crowd, and someone hands him a hammer and chisel. He leans across to Harry and holds the tip of the chisel to the top of her forehead.

"No!" I cry out, but he brings the hammer down hard. Harry makes no sound, no movement, but for the tears rolling from her stony eyes. The boy smashes away at the chisel, over and over, until a crack forms in Harry's head. Her face comes away and falls to the floor. The boy lifts his foot above what's left of her face and stomps down hard, leaving just a pile of rubble.

"Next," he says.

The bruising hands on my arms release and I almost fall, but someone grabs around my waist. Danny is by my side, holding me up, saving me. Relief floods through my body and I manage a breath.

But he walks me into the centre of the room, his grip tightening as I realise what's happening. He's part of this.

And I'm next.

My breaths turn to shallow gasps.

"Danny, let go." My sweaty hands claw at his fingers. "Why are you doing this?"

"To live forever," he answers.

He takes my shoulders and forces me down. My knees buckle and I'm made to kneel beside the faceless lump of stone that used to be my sister.

The boy in the ill-fitting suit steps to one side and a man in a tracksuit, the sports teacher, walks up to me. He hunches forward, his silver pendant dangling between us, two silver spirals.

I try to stand but Danny keeps me down, his knee between my shoulder blades. The mouth of the sports teacher opens; a fast spreading crescent of luminous blue light.

"Cover your pretty face," Danny's whispers in my ear.

I throw my hands up quickly. Cold fingers stab at my lips, prising open my mouth. Something climbs inside my throat.

I can't breathe.

I'm frozen solid, too heavy and exhausted to try to fight back. With the last of my energy I spread my fingers and peek through the gaps. The sports teacher's mouth is wide open, his tongue wagging through the pulsating blue light entering him.

My light.

His mouth closes and my vision goes blank.

I'M STILL ALIVE, SOME SMALL PART OF ME, BUT I DON'T think I should be. I wish I wasn't. I'm outside. I feel the passing of the seasons, the warmth of the sun and the sting of winter ice. Time is different, it moves both fast and slow. I hear voices sometimes. I've tried to scream to them, but I've long since given up. I never make a sound. Most of the voices are unfamiliar, girls blindly following Latford boys inside the church. Then the screams. There are always screams. But sometimes I hear him, that addictive, teasing voice that belongs to Danny. And I look forward to the sweet scent of nicotine as he passes my cowering statue and blows smoke through my stone fingers, into my face.

A Weekend Away Retold

JAMES SOUZE

I AM A LONELY OLD MAN AND, AFTER BOTCHED PROSTATE surgery, my penis is useless. My children and grandchildren visit when they can but they have their own lives to lead. What a way to start a memoir? A story based on imperfect recollections, some fact, some fiction. The story that I want to tell you about me.

For a long time I have been fascinated by the idea that the world, as I experience it, only exists in my mind. It is the sum of the sensory inputs made real by my brain and experienced by my mind. Your world is entirely different. It is more than us having different perspectives on the same event. We have different experiences of the same event. Which is why this is the story that I want to tell you about me. My construction of events.

I can't decide if my memoirs will be a confessional, or a rationalisation of events and decisions, or a celebration, or a sombre reflection. I have hurt people. I have been hurt. I like to think that I have been wronged more often than I have wronged others, but I suspect that is a fallacy. How best to cover the sweep of time and geography, and explain myself to you:

in retrospect with perfect hindsight clarity; in episodes with amusing anecdotes to engage you; as an arc through my life from birth to now, described as a rational progression and not just happenstance?

It's really the storytelling that interests me. We all tell stories to ourselves and to each other. In the stories we explain, expand, rationalise and justify. Reconstructing events to present ourselves in the way that we want to be seen. I want to be seen as a "good guy" but, if I'm honest, there's sufficient evidence to suggest otherwise. Let me tell you one story to explain.

It was a weekend away. Many years ago now but re-lived many times over in my mind. Even now I can feel the warm sun, cold sea, taste the barbecued food and crisp beer, not to mention the au pair! A blissful weekend, or was it?

A weekend away with University friends, by the sea, no plans beyond a cricket match to watch, a sleeping bag and a promise of somewhere to sleep. It started well with a train journey. Is there a better way to travel to the seaside for a holiday?

I'm not so old that the steam train took me to the water's edge on some tourist branch line, stepping out in an all-in-one woollen swimsuit! Imagine more a man in his forties. Tired, weighed down by failed expectations and daily expectations yet to be met, or missed. Plagued by the word *should*: should be a good husband; should be a good father; should work hard; should be slim, fit and healthy; should have a better work-life balance; ad infinitum, ad nauseam. It would be many years and a few crises before I knew better.

Do you know *If–* by Rudyard Kipling? The nation's favourite poem or some other such nonsense. To me it's not an inspiration. It's a litany of impossible feats that, if not achieved, mean that "you'll [not] be a Man, my son." Tragic. And so against that background and with that baggage; I took a train, to the seaside, for a weekend away.

I find the train distracting and hypnotic with its swaying rhythm and percussion track. Soon the city slipped away behind me and the countryside whisked me along, bathed in Friday sunshine and anticipation. These friends, the best of friends from the best of times: university before it all got too expensive and serious. Three years of fun punctuated with just enough study not to fail and then the climactic cramming sessions for finals, followed by the long slow summer of graduation before adulthood.

We hadn't seen each other for years, many years but that wouldn't matter. These were the best of friends. That's how I explained it to my wife, and indirectly to my children. Just one weekend away, you don't really know them, it's a long journey, Maybe I should go by myself? That was true, not a manipulation, but, as you'll see—quite convenient.

Before long the daily commuters had left the train and just the holidaymakers were left. Still no one spoke but you could feel the mood lift. The weather forecast was good and the seaside was rushing towards us—well as much as an old diesel train rushes anywhere! I started to make a plan. Fish and chips for supper with something to wash it down: middle-aged half-price wine (white for fish, of course) or student cans of Australian lager or bloke-ish bottles of real ale? I decided on wine, as a pseudo-gift, and beer, plenty of it.

I arrived at the house with my sleeping bag, wine, beer and baggage. It was time to party! It didn't start well.

The house, a dowdy seaside bungalow, was full of people I didn't know and they didn't look like they were having fun. I was handed a cup of tea. I accepted and made small talk, getting to know people whilst wondering where on Earth my friends were and was my weekend going to live up to expectations?

There were going to be more people involved in this weekend than just my University friends and I. It was going to involve their children, aged parents and people I didn't know. Not to worry. I was sufficiently gregarious to cope, although big parties aren't really my idea of fun. I prefer to talk to people and not about football or any other such banality. As one of my favourite quotes says: I like to party, and when I say party I mean read books. Alone. But I was away for a weekend, by the sea, to see friends and my learned social skills would mean it would be fine.

Fine. Feelings inside not expressed.

Dinner it turned out was "help yourself to the chilli on the stove" which, by the time I got to it, was mostly split beans, watery sauce and some dried-out rice. I made my excuses and drifted out of the house towards the village and chip shop. Feeling better already.

Seaside villages are amongst my favourite places. It doesn't matter what the season is, they always have something to recommend them. The evening and the village were perfect for my mood. It was a summer evening with the warmth left over from the day that makes any stroll pleasant. The few passers-by and gaggle of teenagers in the bus shelter reminded me of wistful teenage summer evenings hoping for an elusive holiday romance.

I bought my fish and chips and headed to the beach. A picturesque sandy bay with classic rocky buttresses and strolling couples. I settled on a rock to savour my food and my mood. A little self-indulgent you might say but few things are as good as your own company in the right place with pleasant distractions. The sea kissed the beach and I remembered teenage kisses on a beach.

Chilled by the sea breeze I returned to the bungalow. All was not well. A child was sick. The parents (my friends) and grandparents were worried. There was talk of doctors and hospital visits but where and how in a rural county at the weekend? It was decided that my friends would take their child to the hospital. A good decision: the child was sick and the indecision wasn't helping any of us! So they left. Being the good friend that I am I played host, made cups of tea, listened to the worried grandparents and lent them money for a taxi to their hotel. All of which I was genuinely happy to do. It felt good. I'm a good guy. I crawled into my sleeping bag in a small tent on a slope in the back garden and fell asleep.

I woke with the sun, rested and looking forward to really getting on with my weekend away with my friends. It was early and the house was quiet. After a while the au pair, Kirsty, came down for breakfast. It turned out the child was really sick. It was staying in hospital and my friends weren't expected to be back for a while, may be not until after the weekend. I must admit I was pissed off. Time, money and effort spent on a weekend away that wasn't to be.

I returned to Kirsty. I hadn't really noticed her the night before but in pyjamas and with tousled hair, she caught my attention. Maybe the weekend could be different, an elusive holiday romance with new kisses on the beach? No. That was wrong. I was married. I didn't travel to the seaside to have an affair. I'm a good guy who should, who would be faithful.

Saturday turned out to be wonderful. I spent it with Kirsty, at the beach, watching cricket, drinking beer, cooking together and relaxing over simple food. Time well spent with a good companion, more than that a gorgeous companion. The light attached itself to her like a radiant hug that made her glow. She quickened my heart and my wit. To this very day I still feel her essence, and my heart still responds as I write this, even though it was just a day that time has diluted many times over like a homeopath's remedy.

That night in my tent, alone I hasten to add, Kirsty was in my mind and my dreams. I was faithful, although I guess that depends on your definition of fidelity? Is it just physical or mental and physical fidelity? I can manage the first but not the second. It's too easy to fall in love with the idea of a girl. Reality is always messier, more complicated and rarely as satisfying.

That's how I awoke the next morning, Sunday, indulging in a brief mental, unrequited love affair. The daydream rudely shattered by the child. It was back, no longer sick and desperate to go to the beach. It sounded awful. Time to leave. There was nothing left in the weekend for me. It had been nothing that I had expected and so much more than I expected.

The story doesn't end there. I had to return home to my wife and children, as a good husband, faithful and honest. What to say? What story to tell about my actions and thoughts, about my weekend away? I spent the whole journey back constructing and reconstructing a version of events. Only one story would do. It had to be both true and present me as a good guy, good friend and faithful husband. All the things I wanted to be, that I should be. The first telling of the story wasn't the same as this construction. That story wasn't as nuanced as this re-telling.

By now I tell myself that it wasn't a less honest version, just less specific. Today I'm telling you about my weekend away in more detail so that you can agree that I was a good guy, even in the face of temptation and trying circumstances. For that is how I want you to see me.

Cuke

LUKE EDLEY

FOR AS LONG AS I CAN REMEMBER, I'VE ALWAYS WANTED to be a porn star.

'Callum!' shouted Isaac in his booming West African trill, pointing to a sealed cardboard box on the floor. 'Quit daydreaming. Come on. Get stacking, boy!'

I've been working as a part-time pharmacy assistant for a good few months now, just to earn myself a few bob while studying for my A-levels.

Basically, they're paying me peanuts to keep the dispensary shelves stacked up with prescription drugs, ready to be shoved like dolly mixture down the throats of pill-popping old codgers to keep them docile.

My job is piss easy—a monkey could do it. Trouble is, people pay good money to see monkeys in zoos, but they won't pay me more than £3.87 an hour because I'm not eighteen yet. Fucking bastards.

After carrying the box to the back of the pharmacy, I tore it open with a pair of scissors—inside, I found a pick 'n' mix of the NHS's familiar favourites, such as Zolmitriptan, Tramadol and Warfarin. I switched into stock-rotating mode.

Anyway, where was I? Oh yes. Porn stardom. Instead of trading Pokémon cards in school, most of my youth was spent cutting out pictures of Page 3 girls and smuggling them into class.

Typing out the word BOOBS on a calculator became a regular habit as I started to wonder what a real pair of them felt like. It wasn't until later I discovered they feel exactly like the silicon gel on a mouse-pad wrist-rest. Soft and squidgy.

'How you doing, Callum?'

'Er, just starting.'

Discovering wanking in my early teens was my real Damascene moment. It was at that moment I understood the truly defining moment of all human achievement – a raging orgasm. You can take all the school exams in the world but nothing compares to a good belly-splattering every now and again.

That's when it really started for me. I even managed to chip my older brother's PlayStation to play a pirated porn game where you could use your controller to perform sex acts on a blonde chick—you could even finger her snatch. It's a million miles from squashing a mushroom in Super Mario, let me tell you that.

Naturally, being distracted by such pubescent urges meant I eventually went on to flunk my GCSE in Maths, but I left school with enough knowledge to know that 2 plus 2 equals a boner.

'You best be halfway through that box, Callum,' Isaac warned me. 'You know how it is. The Devil makes work for idle hands, y'know? Chop chop!'

'Sorry, boss.'

After many masturbatory revelations, I started shoplifting porn mags from the off licence on a regular basis. I read a book about John Holmes and the 1,001 things he did with his gargantuan cock before spoiling everybody's fun by dropping dead of AIDS. I also learnt about how Linda Lovelace effectively turned nobgobbling into an art form.

Being a child of the internet generation, it wasn't long before I found myself voraciously scouring the web for porn sites, absorbing each audio-visual orgasmic experience with my mouth gaping open like I was watching a fucking concerto by the Royal Philharmonic Orchestra.

Now I know what you're thinking. Surely a guy with an unhealthy interest in sex who harbours aspirations of porn stardom is doomed to a life of bachelorhood?

On the contrary, I do have a girlfriend. Her name is Jade. Admittedly, I've not lost my virginity yet, but Jade and I have been dating for about a month and she is actually coming over to stay tonight.

My parents have kindly agreed to fuck off out of the house for the evening so I can have my wicked way with Jade and put into practice all of the tricks of the porn trade I've been picking up over all these years.

I hope she's ready for it. We've been sexting quite a lot. She's even got her tits out on Snapchat, so I'm guessing I've moistened her up enough for a night of penetrative frolicking.

I reached into the cardboard box for the next stack of pills to shelve. It was Amoxycillin—I ambled around to the A section of the pharmacy which brought me standing shoulder to shoulder with Isaac.

'How are things at home, Callum?' Isaac asked, with a curious smirk.

Originally hailing from Nigeria, Isaac practically had PhDs coming out of his arse. Even if you had rigor mortis he'd probably have some idea of how to get you up on your feet again.

'Not too bad, thanks,' I said.

'And how's that girlfriend of yours?'

'Oh, she's great. Actually, she's staying over my place tonight.'

Isaac laughed. 'Lucky you! A night of passion awaits.'

I pretended to behave like a gentleman and bit my lip.

'Here, let me give you some advice, my friend,' Isaac said. 'Do you want to know the secret to a long and happy relationship?'

I nodded. 'Sure.'

'Cucumber,' came Isaac's reply. 'If you eat a whole cucumber before the act of making love, you will get a rock hard erection.'

Isaac made a gesture with his fist and his forearm.

I was intrigued.

'Cucumber. Really? Is that what they eat in Nigeria?'

'No,' said Isaac. 'My brothers and sisters don't eat anything in Nigeria. They starve to death.'

Isaac watched my gormless expression before breaking into a beaming smile and laughing uproariously.

'I'm just kidding with you! You white boys are so gullible.'

Picking up the prescription he was preparing, Isaac chuckled to himself before strolling out to greet an impatient old lady waiting for her beta blockers.

I STARTED WORRYING AGAIN. I COULDN'T HELP BUT FEEL a little bit nervous about sex. Even though I'm still a virgin, I've been doing a few things to prepare myself for my night of passion with Jade.

For the last few weeks, I've been tying a fishing weight to my erection and flexing my penis to build up my prostate muscles—apparently this gives you a lot of self-control at the point of ejaculation.

That said, I do have niggling doubts. Since it'll be my first time, there's a part of me which worries my performance won't be as legendary as Ron Jeremy or Seymour Butts.

I knew from my porn-researching habits that some adult film stars snorted Xanax before sex scenes to help them relax and reduce anxiety. I thought maybe a similar stimulant could help me be less worried and more confident.

I have no idea what sort of legit pharmacy drugs would be of any use. Most of the prescriptions we dish out seem to lobotomise grannies like the inmates in Nurse Ratched's ward in *One Flew Over the Cuckoo's Nest*, so I imagine prescription meds wouldn't be sexual performance-enhancers.

For this reason, I decided to find myself a proper drug dealer.

After all, if cocaine made Tony Montana look so cool and so invincible in *Scarface*, then I guessed maybe I could do with some of that Columbian marching powder myself. I'd never tried it before, but time was of the essence.

My plan was to buy some coke and snort it up my schnoz before Jade arrived. That way, I'd be more than ready to give her a night of sweet insouciant boning she'd never forget.

I pulled a black bag out of the bin and saw Isaac return to the dispensary area. 'I've just gotta throw this in the rubbish, boss,' I said, tying a knot in the bag. 'Be back in a sec.'

Isaac mumbled approvingly.

I walked further to the back of the pharmacy, holding the bin bag out in front of me like I was clutching the neck of a dead rabbit.

Towards the rear of the building, I exited the back door to the garden and traipsed the narrow pathway to the wheelie bin.

Throwing the bag inside, I slammed the lid down.

I looked up to see the drug dealer. I had arranged to meet him out here, and he was staring at me from behind the mesh fence, smoking a roll-up cigarette.

I gulped. I was so nervous I could feel my kneecaps rattling like maracas in a salsa bar.

'Listen,' the dealer said. 'I got your message.' He took a puff on his ciggie. 'So what is it you want?'

'Err, I dunno really,' I replied, my voice quavering. 'Some lines…of Charlie? That's what you call it, right?'

'You want coke?'

'Er, yeah, I think so… It–It–It makes you less nervous, right?'

The dealer shrugged. 'Depends. What's the occasion again? You said it was a date with someone, right?'

'Yeah, I'm losing my virginity and I…want to be really good at it.'

Once I said this, I felt a bit embarrassed, but the dealer's icy demeanour seemed to thaw a little at my honesty. 'I see,' he said. 'Well, I've got just the thing. It'll cost you though…'

'Okay,' I said. 'How much do you want?'

The dealer stood silently. 'Let's call it 50 quid,' he replied.

I grabbed for my wallet and handed him some notes, my fingers tremoring.

In one swift movement, the dealer's hand slipped through the gap in the mesh and swiped the money out of my fingers in the blink of an eye.

I looked down at my outstretched palm. Somehow, as if by sleight of hand, the dealer had replaced the notes with a transparent bag of white powder and a tiny glass vial of clear-to-yellowish liquid. I closed my fingers into a fist.

'If it's euphoria you're after, trust me bruv, that'll do it...' he said, tapping his nose. 'Sniff some of that stuff and you'll be proper on it.'

'Is it cocaine?'

'Not quite. Better for you, I think. Let's just say kids like you see this stuff as a rite of passage nowadays. Everybody's doing it.'

'Wow. Thanks,' I said. 'What about this glass thing?

'Be careful with that,' he added. 'The less you know about it, the better. It's a liquid, so you'll need to empty it into a can of Pepsi or summat. Then drink it.'

'And what does it do?'

'Gets rid of any hang-ups. Gets rid of stress. You'll 'ave a good time on it. If you take it at the same time as the powder it'll be one hell of a party.' The dealer was unwilling to stick around for longer than he absolutely had to. 'Anything else?'

I shook my head.

'Well, that's done then,' he replied.

'Pleasure doing business with you.'

'Any time, man. Have a good night.'

I opened my fingers slightly and peeked at the vial of liquid held in my palm.

'Laters, dawg,' I found myself saying, though I'm really not sure why. Street slang isn't exactly my strong suit.

The dealer shook his head as he walked away, leaving me slightly entranced by the vial, in little doubt that such a small thing would make a big difference.

HAVING NOW ACQUIRED THE DRUGS, I COULDN'T SHAKE off Isaac's advice about the cucumber, so I decided to buy one after work.

There was a 2-for-1 special offer on cucumbers in the supermarket, so I threw both of them in my shopping basket. I found it hard to imagine that an elongated, cylindrical culinary vegetable could help me get a stonk on, but if it's good enough for the Nigerians, then it's damn well good enough for me.

After all, the drugs might help get rid of the nerves, but if eating a cuke ensures my little chap is standing to attention, that'd only add to my sexual prowess. With that and the drugs I'd be taking, I'd be all set. This was going to be a doddle. My first real test as an aspiring porn star was upon me.

I arrived home with not a lot of time left to prepare. This house was empty so I was pleased to see Mum and Dad got the hint.

I didn't hang about. I went straight into the kitchen, pulled one of the cucumbers out of my 5p carrier bag and immediately took a huge bite.

The cuke was tougher than I expected, its dark green skin crunching loudly as my incisors bit into it.

The taste almost made me retch, but I forced myself to continue.

Drips of pale, watery green gunk soon started to drip down my chin.

Feeling less like a vegetable and more like a coarse hunk of rubber, it slithered over my tongue as I gagged on its green waxen flesh, a slimy residue coating my teeth with an acrid biofilm.

I starting biting into the shaft speedily like I was taking part in a Bushtucker Trial, munching on it like a parrot pecks at a millet spray.

I was pretty sure you're not supposed to binge on cucumber like this, but Isaac did say I had to eat a whole one.

Cucumber juice kept dripping over my fingers, its bitter taste sloshing in my palette as bits of stray skin lodged between my teeth.

I kept eating until I belched. By this point I'd hit my limit. I'd eaten pretty much three quarters of a cucumber. Surely that'd be enough. I didn't think I could stomach any more. Such a ghastly vegetable.

I picked up a can of Coke and pressed ahead with the next stage of my plan.

Reaching into my pocket, I took out the vial of liquid, unfastened the lid, and poured the mysterious solution into the can.

Unsure how long it'd take to mix, I knew I didn't have much time, so I put it to my lips.

I glugged back a few mouthfuls quickly, if only to get rid of the awful bitter tang of cucumber clinging onto my taste buds, but the Coke tasted a bit saltier than usual.

I checked the time. Jade was due to be here at any minute.

Hastily, I ripped open the bag of white powder and arranged it into a neat line on the kitchen worktop.

I took a deep breath. Then I leaned over and snorted it up my nose.

It had an odd aroma, like a mix of lemon-lime, salt and ammonia, hitting the back of my nasal cavity like a nail bomb of mica flakes.

I half-sneezed. Grasping the can, I downed the remainder of the drink and tried to douse the burning sensation at the back of my throat, even though I couldn't even tell exactly what had caused it.

With the vague taste of cucumber lingering and the bridge of my nose feeling numb from the powder, I knew I was as ready as I'd ever be. All I needed to do now was wait for this bizarre cocktail to work its magic.

I heard the doorbell ring. Bang on time.

Jade was standing in the doorway as I opened the front door. She smiled at me. 'Hey babe,' she said.

'Hi, sexy,' I said. I already felt a little giddy and emboldened by the drugs, and I could already sense my nether regions were being induced into a merry dance of hormones.

Jade was a blonde, rather curvy girl, a size or two up from a perfect ten which is pretty much my type if you were judging me by my most-watched RedTube videos.

Jade tilted her head to one side. 'Are you going to let me in or what?'

I nodded. 'Come on in,' I said. 'Are you thirsty?'

Jade made her way indoors and took off her coat.

'Oh yeah, actually, I could murder a cup of tea.'

'You don't take milk, do you?'

'Yeah.'

'Oh, I'm sorry, we don't have any milk in the house. I'm lactose intolerant.'

'Oh.'

'We have cans of Coke though.'

'Coke will be fine.'

I got Jade a Coke and we did that usual chit-chat bullshit girls seem to adore so much. I won't bore you with the details but I sparked off enough of a conversation so that it made her feel as though I gave a shit about anything other than sex.

It wasn't long, however, before I gestured her to my bedroom. It was almost time for business. Cucumber plus drugs equals impending sexual ecstasy. Tonight marks the start of my new career in porn. I couldn't wait.

I TRIED TO MAKE THE BEDROOM ROMANTIC AND ALL that shit. I lit some stinky Tibetan candles and stuck on a bit of Florence + The Machine on the CD player to set the mood.

Jade immediately knew what she was letting herself in for from the moment she stepped in the bedroom. She stared at me vampishly and approached me with 'fuck me' eyes.

She pressed her tits against me and kissed me tenderly on the lips at first. Then she slipped her tongue between my teeth as she felt both of our hearts begin to race.

Things got frantic pretty fast. I ran my fingers through her hair as we snogged; and in no time at all, her hands drifted down to my groin area, rubbing my already-stiff cock as they pressed against my jeans.

Best I return the favour, I thought. Feeling considerably giddy now from the drugs, I eagerly undid the zipper of her skinny jeans and slipped my finger through her fly and past the lining of her knickers.

I fumbled around the nook of her genitalia until I located the wet lip of her clit.

Relieved I managed to find the right hole, I massaged it as we kissed.

Jade's breathing grew heavy. 'God, I'm so wet,' she said, gazing at me amorously, the look of romance in her eyes.

'Suck it,' I said, pointing to my groin area. Jade stopped sharply and her breathing steadied. She was clearly taken aback.

'Er, sure,' she said, a little bemused.

I undid my jeans and took off my trousers and boxers in a flash.

'Say hello to my little friend,' I said, impersonating Al Pacino. 'Well, big friend…'

Jade knelt down and took my cock in her hand. She started by licking the base of my penis, working her way upwards until she put me in her mouth. Sure enough, it was rock hard— whether that was down to the cuke or the predicament, I can't be too sure.

I put my hands on her head and forced her into me, trying to push my cock further into the back of her throat. She gagged.

'Ugh,' she said, pulling back and wiping her mouth. 'Steady on…'

'Sorry,' I said. 'You don't do deep throating?'

'I think you've been watching too much porn, you naughty boy.'

Jade rose to her feet and unclipped her bra, pulling her top over her head and shoving me onto the bed.

We stripped each other off and shared a brief naked embrace. I kissed her breasts and ran my tongue along her torso, working my way downwards. I gently pulled down her knickers.

She was a lot hairier than the girls I'd been used to seeing on the internet. Still, this was a new experience for me, so I tried not to let it detract from my enjoyment.

I could sense the drugs I'd taken were making me feel a lot bolder.

After gazing up at her tits whilst munching on her pussy like a ghost gobbles up Pac-Man, I simply couldn't stop myself from leaping up her body and clamping my dick between her bosoms and haphazardly attempting a titwank.

She looked surprised.

'Erm, Callum, what the fuck are you doing?'

I stopped. 'Sorry, just a titwank. You have amazing tits.'

'Well, thanks, but tits aren't for wanking. Come on, I'm so wet, let's fuck.'

I was unable to say no to a proposition such as this. I reached out for a condom and quickly put it on my chap, clambering on top of Jade and slipping myself inside her. Considering this was my first time, this felt amazing, even with a condom on. It was so tight, just like clamping my member around a lukewarm hot water bottle made of jelly.

I pumped my dick inside her a few times, until her groans of pleasure distracted me and I almost felt myself cum. At that moment, something unthinkable happened—I burped.

The cuke I had eaten earlier had repeated on me. I burped the distinctly odorous stench of cucumber breath directly into Jade's face. Thankfully, she just laughed.

I pulled out of her, looking deep into her eyes.

'Can I do you from behind?'

She grinned sheepishy. 'Sure, hun.'

Jade turned around; resting on her hands and knees, balancing herself on all fours on the mattress.

She raised her pale arse in the air, her snatch summoning me like a siren beckoning a sailor onto the rocks.

Jade's right hand appeared from beneath her legs and grabbed my cock, guiding me into her.

I thrusted and felt the warm, wet pulp of her vaginal juices oozing around my penis. I let out an involuntary grunt.

It felt different from me being on top: better, tighter, more constricted, like nature's tourniquet squeezing my very essence, tempting me to cum sooner that I wanted to.

Avoiding the almost immediate urge to ejaculate, I stared into space and tried to concentrate on the task at hand. I slid myself inwards, outwards, slowly at first, then faster, then slower again, depending on how strong the urge to cum got with each thrust.

What made it easier to stop myself cumming was the slightly off-putting smell of bum emanating from Jade's arse crack. As horny as she was making me, the whole lovemaking experience was a little on the pongy side—almost as if she'd had sweaty knickers, or failed to wipe herself properly after her last toilet break.

Still, I shouldn't complain. As first times go, this was incredible.

It was only when I felt my lips tingling that I knew something was going wrong.

I could feel the saliva in my mouth going dry.

Despite being inside her, Jade had sensed my enthusiasm was waning and looked at me from over her shoulder. She gasped.

'Holy shit,' she said, pulling away from me so my cock slid out of her. 'What's wrong with your face?'

'Wot yoo meem?' I garbed, seemingly unable to speak plain fucking English.

It was then I realized my lips had swollen and my tongue had inflated to triple size. I could feel my face and chest itching. I began to scratch myself and saw my hands and fingers had become blotchy and pink.

'Your face…' said Jade, 'you look like the fucking hunchback of Notre Dame.'

I caught a glimpse of myself in my bedroom mirror

'Whuh the fuuuh…thith ithnt normuhhl…'

I could see from Jade's expression that she didn't have a clue what was going on. The trouble was, I had lost the capacity to speak, so I couldn't even explain myself.

'Whaaayyyte 'erre…' I said, jumping up off the bed, with my erection flapping around as I ran out of the bedroom.

I decided to run into the kitchen to grab the second cucumber from the carrier bag. I wasn't even sure if the cuke had caused this reaction, but I thought I'd show it to Jade to try and explain what had happened.

I burst back into the bedroom clutching the cucumber. 'Uggghhhhh,' I groaned.

It backfired horribly. Jade wailed in sheer terror; it was obvious the sight of a man bursting into a bedroom brandishing a cucumber while her legs were still open had alarmed her.

'Get the fuck away from me!' she screamed. She scooped up her clothes and made a run for the door.

I tried to pursue her.

'Nooohhhh, waith, ithhh nuuut wot yooooo fink,' I said.

Still naked, I followed her. I made some more incomprehensible noises before I felt a little breathless and my eyesight grew hazy.

As I saw Jade make her way out of the front door, clasping her clothes to her naked chest to cover herself, I fell to my knees.

'Whaaith, thith ith.. uhh..' I collapsed to the floor with my enormous swollen face, my stiffy remaining aloft, in spite of all the chaos.

Helplessly, I saw the front door wide open as Jade ran out naked into the street. My head fell backwards onto the carpet with a thud and I felt my eyes roll back. Next thing I knew, my breathing grew shallower.

Everything went dark. So dark, I assumed I was dead.

THEY RELEASED ME FROM HOSPITAL AFTER A GOOD FEW days, but even that wasn't long enough to get over the embarrassment of being discovered by my parents lying spread-eagled on the floor, stark bollock naked.

The first thing I remember after the incident was waking up bleary-eyed and blinded by bright lights in an emergency ward.

A doctor was hovering over me with a look of concern on his face.

'Wha–what happened?' I said. 'How did I get here?'

'You passed out, Callum. You went into anaphylactic shock.

'Anaphylactic shock?'

'I checked your medical records—you're lactose in-tolerant, correct?'

'Yes.'

'Well, it seems you had an allergic reaction to the cucumber you ate. Unbeknownst to you, in some instances, the wax coating on cucumber contains a protein called milk casein.'

'What? Cucumbers contain milk?!'

'Not quite, it's a hidden protein—it's within the edible wax we find in cucumbers. Milk casein can very rarely trigger adverse reactions in people who are extremely allergic to milk-based food products—I'm presuming that's why your lips, mouth and throat swelled up. It also explains the rashes.'

'But why did I pass out?'

'That's a little trickier to explain. Do you often eat cucumbers, Callum?'

'No. Never.'

'Just as I thought. The swelling in your face and lips indicates you're allergic to plant chemicals called salicylates. Cucumbers are very rich in salicylates, and in some cases this can cause wheezing, hives and—in worst case scenarios, such as yours—anaphylaxis.'

'So I'm allergic to cucumber. Great.'

The doctor arched his eyebrow.

'The drugs in your system wouldn't have helped either.'

'Oh…you know about that?'

'We found traces of mephedrone and gamma-hydroxybutyric acid in your kitchen, so we ran a few blood tests while you were unconscious…'

'What? I didn't even know what they were, I swear…'

'I am not here to judge. But there is a mixture of factors at play there which precipitated your loss of consciousness. I advise you to be more careful in the future. I'm sure you can explain yourself once you've had some rest.'

I slept for hours at a time, but later awoke stinking of stale piss and wringing with sweat, largely due to the mephedrone (otherwise known as meow meow) eeking out through my pores, or so I'm told. The smell clung onto me for days.

It wasn't too long before my mother visited me in hospital.

'Oh, Callum,' my Mum said. 'Why didn't you just tell us?'

'Excuse me?'

'Why didn't you tell us you were gay?'

'What?'

'Listen, your Dad and I think it's wonderful. There's no point denying it. The doctor told us the drugs you took—M-CAT and GHB—are apparently very popular at gay 'chemsex' parties. Is that why you wanted us to go out? So you could have some special time with your boyfriend?'

'Mum,' I implored. 'I'm not gay, okay?'

'Well, you shouldn't feel the need to hide these things. Your Dad and I have a very open mind about this. It's the 21st century—it's unhealthy to keep these sexual feelings bottled up. We just want you to be responsible is all.'

I tried to explain, but in the end, I stopped arguing with her. Mum had convinced herself. But there was one thing she had failed to mention.

The cuke.

As I sat locked in my bedroom at home after being released from hospital, I couldn't stop wondering whether I'd imagined the whole cucumber allergy thing or not. Was it all just a drug-induced fantasy? Was the doctor just a hallucination?

Eventually, I ventured through the house to search for the missing cucumber. I raided the fridge. I knelt down on the floor to see if it fell out of my hand and rolled under the furniture, or the tables.

Nope, still no sign.

I hunted high and low, rummaging throughout all the rooms in the house, but still I could not locate the missing cuke.

Then a horrifying thought stuck me.

There was one room I hadn't checked—my parents' bedroom.

After noticing the door slightly ajar, I gingerly pushed it open.

It was at that moment I saw it—a lone cucumber resting on my Mum and Dad's bedside table next to a tube of KY jelly.

Such a ghastly vegetable.

The Lickspittle Leviathan

DAVID GRIMSTONE

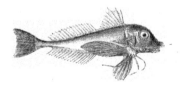

SUNLIGHT WASHED OVER THE SOUTHERN ISLAND OF Lick, lending a terrible scene the sort of sharp contrast most of the observers could have done without.

It was like some sickening jigsaw of a man: all the pieces were there, they just didn't quite fit together in the right way. This was mainly because the edges were wrinkly and, in several places, enthusiastically chewed.

Hieronymus Blush, journeyman magician and newly initiated outreach merchant for the southern islands, stepped between the two grizzled fisherman in order to get a better look at the corpse.

He'd seen a lot of tragic accidents in his five years as an apprentice at the Magician's Proving Ground, but these mostly involved the victims disappearing without a trace. For some reason, the look of complete shock on the face of the corpse was particularly unsettling.

Nevertheless, Blush made a valiant attempt to pull himself together: something the poor native on the beach would never get another go at.

He focused on the sand, drawing a small circle distractedly with his big toe while pointing a thin finger at the body. 'I don't understand why he's...complete?'

All eyes turned to Ryerson, the slightly senior of the two elderly fishermen.

'He's all there because sharks don't like the taste of us,' the old man muttered, suppressing a burp.

Blush boggled at him. 'They don't?'

'No. Unfortunately, by the time they remember that, you're already in five different pieces.'

'Oh.'

Blush took several steps back and beckoned the tribal translator away from the scene. The young native wandered over, leaving the two fishermen to fill their pipes and argue over various aspects of the kill.

'New bad,' the translator growled. 'Not old bad. New bad.'

Blush glanced toward the tree line, and shook his head. He could see the vague outline of human shapes moving through the undergrowth, and had no doubt that the rest of the tribe were keenly observing the scene.

'I won't lie to you,' Blush said, when the tribal translator caught his eye. 'This is a bloody mess, and I'm not just talking about *him on the sand*. That special underground fruit your lot produce is in seriously short supply, and the merchants are up in arms. We can't wait another fortnight for the next batch.'

The native, who was possessed of far too much muscle for one so young, adjusted his loincloth and seemed to take a sudden and unnatural interest in the tip of his spear. Blush suspected, and not for the first time, that the translator was fearfully bright. He looked down at the curious fish anklet that adorned the boy's left leg, and wondered if he could be bribed.

'Do you understand what I'm saying? What's bad for us is bad for you. Unless—'

'No bloodfruit.'

'Are you deliberately *trying* to destroy this island's only solid trade? I don't think the chief would want—'

'NO BLOODFRUIT. PEOPLE SCARED. KILL NEW BAD.'

'Can I speak to the chief? I know he doesn't speak plain tongue, but I was told that the witch doctor is quite fluent—'

'No. You speak ME. Me alone.'

'Fine.' Blush held back the torrent of abuse he wanted to hurl forth, but something about the half smile on the translator's thick lips was giving him the creeps. 'They told me the translator was an old man, so you must be quite new here, yes? Just passed the big test or something, have you?'

The translator stared back at him, unblinking. 'You and men from your city kill New Bad…if you can. Only then Bloodfruit.'

Blush opened and shut his mouth a few times before mooching over to the rejoin the fishermen.

'Well?' he snapped. 'It's a shark: I assume we can find the bastard and kill it easily enough?'

The younger of the pair, a sprightly octogenarian called Jed, knelt beside the head of the corpse and stared up at him myopically. 'We'll have a go,' he said, 'but there's something amiss with this as far as shark attacks go. Can't you see what's strange here?' He reached down, took hold of the head and pushed back a chewed fold of the upper lip. 'It's taken his teeth.'

THE FISH SLICER KUMATRA, FOURTH SON OF A THIRD nephew on his mother's side, sat on the rocks of Lickspittle Bay and performed the one task for which he held a great tribal responsibility. He sliced fish.

He sliced the fat ones.

He sliced the thin ones.

He sliced the ones that some of his more questionable cousins found strangely attractive.

Kumatra looked behind him at the generous pile of fish that constituted the morning's third haul.

Odd.

It was half the size it had been just a few seconds before.

Kumatra flipped onto his feet, tightened his grip on the filleting knife and padded over to the big flat rock he used as a base for his net.

There were two big holes in the side of the twine mesh, and a lot of the fish were splashing into the water: even the attractive ones.

Kumatra muttered under his breath, and crouched to snatch back the edge of the net.

He was just hauling part of the mesh over the base of the rock when a sleek green shark leaped out of the water and bit him in half.

A spray of blood fountained into the air, and Kumatra's legs remained standing for a few seconds while the rest of the fish flopped into the ocean.

The shark darted away.

THE BOAT SLOWLY CIRCLED THE ISLAND, SKULKING through shallow waters as a series of inlet bays and ancient monuments drifted past.

Blush had never seen a giant statue in the shape of an octopus before, but the heathen tribes of the southern islands worshipped strange gods. There were rumours of underwater cities, subterranean caves dripping with the blood of human sacrifice and even the odd story about natives interbreeding with some of the more attractive fish.

I need to find this thing quickly, he reminded himself. *Otherwise, I'll be spending a night around the campfire with these filthy...Lickers.*

'I don't think much of the equipment,' he said aloud, folding his arms in a dissatisfied manner while attempting to avoid falling over the side of the boat. 'I take it you two are usually on a budget?'

Jed ignored the question and continued to the heave at the rudder lever, but Ryerson immediately stomped over to where the magician was standing.

'It's a decent enough cog,' he muttered. 'Square-rigger, strong rudder: a proper whaling craft. None of that stripped-down wood rot you get from Breakers' Yard up in Dullitch.'

Blush heaved a sigh, and pointed towards the edge of the deck.

'I'm not talking about the boat, Ryerson: I'm talking about that load of old junk you've brought along! You're supposed to be expert shark hunters, for crying out loud.'

'And?'

'Well, it's hardly an arsenal, is it?' Blush gestured emphatically at the small and rather pathetic collection of weapons in the rolled out cloth bundle behind the elderly fisherman. There was a small lump-hammer, a hand axe, a kitchen knife and a small bottle of something that he fancied might have been brandy. 'It's a killer shark we're dealing with; not a bunch of rowdy market traders.'

Ryerson took a drag on the misshapen pipe that drooped from his lips. 'You need to understand that your best possible chance of taking down a predator in these islands is to engage the beast in close combat. All this running away scared and screaming nonsense just gives them a stronger sense of purpose. If they take the leg off a man and that man keeps on punching them in the face, often times they'll give the whole thing up as a bad job. Way back when I was a boy, I knew a man that got attacked by a shark out beyond the eastern reef. That shark took a hold of him and sunk its teeth into his very soul, but he wasn't having any of it. You know what he did? He ran right out of the water with the beast still clinging to his right leg, and he stamped it to death on the sand. What do you think of that?'

'I think it's a completely ridiculous story, and I think that you just made it up. I also think that there's a good chance all three of us are going to die if you're genuinely intending to go into hand to fin combat with a shark that just made a *jigsaw* out of a man who, judging by his component body parts, was the size of a bloody ogre.'

Ryerson spat a hefty wad of phlegm at the magician's feet.

'Well, if 'un that's the case then it's a ver' good job we have a magic user to watch over us…now isn't it?'

Blush wrapped an arm around the mast before rolling up his opposing sleeve and displaying an open palm for the two fishermen to see. As he stared intently at the space in front his hand, a tiny glimmering ball of red light appeared within, swelling and swirling as it reached a higher level of intensity.

'I am a journeyman on the path of Fire Magic,' he commented. 'The burning intensity of my particular school of conjuration is feared by many, many creatures from all over Illmoor.' He leaned forward and gritted his teeth. 'I'm afraid that *fish* are not among them.'

THE TRIBE WAS OUT IN FORCE FOR THE MID-AFTERNOON ritual. This was a particularly important event, as it was well documented that the mid-afternoon gods often went off the deep end if they were given less whaling hymnals than the sunrise bunch.

If anything, the latest ritual was looking likely to be more dramatic than usual. It wasn't every day that the tribal witchdoctor, Bodiker, made a personal appearance on the sand.

Dressed in a full garb of feathers and boasting curious bark earrings and an angular fish mask, Bodiker was a sight to behold: preferably through a long range spyglass.

He danced, shimmied, sidestepped, convulsed and somersaulted in front of the tribe as they formed a sort of human snake on their journey to the water's edge...

...but he didn't quite make it to the water before an enormous ocean spray stopped him dead in his tracks.

The ocean swelled up and flumed a second time, exploding over the beach like an angry cobra darting for its prey.

This time, however, it spewed forth the rotted, half chewed and entirely toothless head of Kumatra, the fish slicer.

A series of frantic cries erupted from the conga-line as word spread among the tribe of this new horror that had been cast among them. Villagers ran in every direction as panic took hold of the natives' collective consciousness, dripping the poison of fear into each and every mind.

Only Bodiker stood firm on the sea-hammered sands of Lick, his expression firm and his eyes devoid of all wonder.

The old witchdoctor looked out at the solitary, fast receding fin of the island's savage predator and thought: *I know who you are.*

He glanced back at his retreating horde, and tried to figure out which member of the tribe was missing.

IT WAS, BEYOND ANY SHADOW OF A DOUBT, AN ELDERLY dog.

Blush decided that to call the thing a bloodhound would have made the presumption that it had some measure of blood *in* it: a fact put in doubt by the pale jowls, rheumy eyes and lack of effort it seemed to exude with every movement.

'Are you sure this thing can track a shark?' he prompted, as Ryerson led the exhausting looking hound from the depths of the boat's ramshackle cabin. 'Only, it looks like it might not last the night.'

'Don't you worry about Dash,' shouted Jed from the back of the boat. 'He can smell a blood trail a mile away...even in water.'

'DASH?'

Ryerson glared at the magician as if daring him to challenge the validity of the dog's name. 'Yep.'

The senior fisherman unclasped the dog's wiry chain and whistled between his teeth. It was a shrill, pitchy note: the sort that made your teeth hurt.

To Blush's amazement, the dog immediately took a run up and vaulted over the side of the boat, hitting the water with a detonating splash.

Jed and Ryerson both dawdled to the starboard side of the boat and began to whoop and cheer in a most excited fashion while Blush worried about whether or not the craft would tip over if he crossed the deck to join them. After what seemed like a lifetime, however, he managed to crane his neck in order to get a good view of the dog that was now making a spirited effort to lead them in what had to be a completely random direction (as no disenchanted animal could possibly pick up any sort of trail at such speed). He started to wonder, once again, whether the two fisherman were possessed of a full ticket between them...or even half a ticket, come to that.

Jed quickly hobbled across the deck and took a firm grip on the rudder lever, swinging the wooden handle around and hauling on it with all his might.

The boat lurched and moved into a steep turn: they were now forging straight for a deserted reef a short distance from the main island.

'The natives call it Notmuch Atoll,' said Ryerson, squinting as he pointed a bony finger at the atoll. 'It's a haven for sharks. I got this out on Notmuch in my youth.' He bunched one hand into a fist and knocked hard on his right leg: there was a hollow, wooden sound.

Blush just stared at him.

'What?' Ryerson demanded. 'Don't pity me, boy. Young Jed over there has two.'

'You're NOT serious.'

'Deadly.'

'You have *three* wooden legs between you? I'm so glad I went with the Fisherman's Guild for this job: there's absolutely no substitute for having confidence in the people you're working with.'

'He's got something! He's GOT SOMETHING!' Jed was yelling and pointing ahead of the boat, where it seemed that Dash had paddled to the shore and trotted *out of the water*. 'I'm telling you: he's on the trail! We're going in!'

The dog had exploded from the lapping waves and was now beginning to pick up the pace. It sprang over the sands with an excitement bordering on lunacy and was now crossing the curved atoll like a demented racehorse.

Blush tripped and fell in an effort to scramble to the front of the boat.

'But he's heading onto the atoll! It's a lagoon island! For the love of all sanity, we're supposed to be chasing a SHARK! What did it do, dive out of the ocean and run onto dry land?'

Ryerson reached down and snatched a handful of Blush's hair, yanking his head to the right.

'You mean like *that*, Mister Magician?'

Blush stared out at the atoll, and swallowed. He was looking at a sight he wouldn't ever have believed was possible within the framework of the civilized world. He was looking at an image that would stay burned into his head until the day he boarded that mist-bound ship to Parts Unknown. He was looking...at a sleek green shark running across dry land on two incredible muscular human legs.

Blush opened and closed his mouth a few times, but no sound came out.

The shark was complete: the head, midsection, fins and tail were all present. In that respect, it was very much a shark... with the slight difference that this *particular* member of the species could enter a marathon with a better than average chance of getting onto the podium.

It was just...wrong.

The legs were obviously jutting from the undercarriage in some hideous mutation that simply had to be the result of the sort of interbreeding Blush didn't even want to think about.

Surely, even as a native of Lick, *you had to draw the line somewhere.*

The thought persisted as the front of the boat thunked into the atoll's rocky outcropping.

Ryerson hurried over to the weapons, took the hammer and the knife for himself and tossed the miniature axe to Jed. When neither of them made a move for the whiskey, Blush scrambled over on his hands and knees to grab the bottle himself.

Despite their age and the fact that three quarters of their running appendages were wooden, the two fishermen moved with surprising alacrity. Blush had to use a minor fire conjuration on his ankles in an attempt to put in the kind of effort that didn't make him look pathetically unfit by comparison.

However, several factors quickly conspired to slow him down. Apart from the difficulty he'd always had wading through any body of water that went above the knee-line, and the fact that he was struggling to catch his breath, there was the moderately alarming scene now unfolding on the beach up ahead.

Dash had closed in on his prey, but the bloodhound had sensibly decided to slow to a soft pad as he drew near to the shark, which had—against everyone's expectations—suddenly turned around and was standing its ground. On the two legs that more than ably supported its frame, the Lickspittle Leviathan looked like a giant, hovering wasp full of razor sharp teeth... and the dog had evidently reached such a great age by quickly handing all prey over to the experts.

The experts in question were now staggering, limping and hobbling towards the killer beast, waving their respective weapons in a manner that did nothing for Blush's sense of confidence in them as highly trained whalers.

Jed reached the creature first, and took two mighty swings at it with the hand axe. The first one missed when the demonic, freakish thing hotfooted a speedy dodge, but the second one connected and stuck fast in its flank. Jed made a move to retrieve the axe, but the shark immediately went on the attack, kicking the old man swiftly between the legs and, when he doubled up, biting his head clean off. Blood volcanoed out of the opening in the newly ravaged neck and the rest of Jed's body collapsed in a heap.

Blush skidded to a halt, cried out in horror and, ripping the cork from the whiskey bottle, took several big gulps before emptying the remaining contents over his hands. Then, amid much coughing and spluttering, he began to mutter under his breath: the magic caught, spurred on and increased by the alcohol as the flames began to spring from his pores.

The shark and Ryerson were circling each other, looking for an opening. Ryerson was reaching back with the hammer, but had the knife twitching and turning in front of him, his hands moving quickly to suggest that they were capable of a lot of damage in only one or two strikes. The shark on the other hand, was just slowly pacing along, grinning manically: it had no choice.

Ryerson struck out, ducking under the great-headed torso to plunge the knife deep into the beast's underbelly. At the same time, he swung the hammer around and brought it into a rising trajectory, catching his prey with an uppercut that knocked it sideways.

Unfortunately, it was then that the old man made what turned out to be a cardinal mistake. He turned and ran.

The shark leaped after him, bowling him over and biting down hard on his wooden leg.

Ryerson screamed and clawed at the sand, trying to escape the prowling wrath of the mutant predator by kicking at it with his good foot…but even Blush could see that the next bite was going to be the last one.

Still mumbling cursed enchantments through trembling lips, Ryerson barely noticed as Dash, no stranger to danger and evidently a lot smarter than his owners, bulleted past in the opposite direction.

Ryerson had rolled onto his back and was frantically kicking and screaming, but the shark wasted no time, finishing him off by dropping onto its own ridiculous knees and biting him cleanly in two. It would have been the most horrific slaughter Blush had ever seen *had he actually seen it*…but the magician was halfway to another dimension, his eyes engorged with the magical fuel that now birthed a fireball the size of his chest.

The shark leaped onto its feet and bolted forward, running at the distant figure with a demonic intent so clear and purposeful that it almost created a scene of beauty to behold.

Blush shook himself from his reverie when the creature was still about fifty feet away from him. Then he simply released the ball of flame and watched it seer into the shark with an incredible explosion of heat and light.

The shark collapsed onto the sand and began to writhe around, one leg blazing merrily as it careered from side to side.

It was then that Blush noticed the familiar looking fish anklet on the burning leg.

Mother of all mercy, Blush thought. *It's the translator. This...thing...is the boy I was speaking to.*

Blush felt a fleeting burst of pity for the terrible creature before it suddenly dawned on him firstly that the shark wasn't going to die and secondly that he needed time to prepare another attack. He backed away from the wretched creature that was desperately trying to flip, kick and scrape its way back into the water. Then he turned and ran for the safety of the jungle.

THE TRIBE WERE GATHERED AROUND AN ANCIENT cooking pot when Blush arrived, puffing and panting, on the edge of the village. One by one, each of the villagers retreated inside their huts or hurried for the comparative protection of the main cave system. Only the tribal chief and Bodiker, the witch doctor, remained at the pot, both wearing the sort of sour, guilty expressions men always get when past wrongs return to plague the blissful ignorance of oblivious lives.

'Right. *Who is he...*and don't give me any more heathen guff or else I'll report back to the merchant guilds and hiding the bloodfruit will be the least of your worries: you'll end up with an army on your doorstep.'

Bodiker and the chief exchanged glances, and a few words in the tribal dialect.

'Come on!' Blush prompted, gesturing towards the witch-doctor. 'I know *you* speak plain tongue. *Who is he?'*

Bodiker removed his headdress and dipped a hand into the pot, fishing around distractedly for some delicacy that apparently eluded him.

'It's a shapechanger,' he said, his voice showing no signs of humour. 'I know of only one other creature that hungered for human teeth for its transformative powers…and it was the parent of this one.'

'But, listen—your translator…'

'…is the beast. Yes. What we feared has come to pass.'

'You KNOW?'

'We can assume. I have lost two sons today, Mister Blush. You inspected the body of my oldest child this morning, and my other son went missing this afternoon while cutting fish for the tribe. This plague upon our people…is my own doing, and my own punishment.'

Blush straightened up, slightly mollified by the evidence of some apparent honesty. 'I'm listening.'

Bodiker stepped away from the pot and fell onto his knees.

'Several years ago, a man was shipwrecked here on Lick. He claimed to be a fugitive from the mainland. We tended his wounds and restored him to health: he became one of us. He had—how do you people say it—a *talent*…for the teeth?'

'A dentist?'

'As you would say it, yes…but it was soon revealed that he did, in fact, hunger for the very ivories he claimed able to treat. He was discovered, caught red handed and bloody mouthed. When we confronted him, he changed his shape in order to evade capture, revealing a variety of diabolical talents. He was a curse, an abomination. He was cruel, and broken, and he liked to inflict pain: the tribe suffered terrible anguish as a result of his stay here.'

Blush nodded, noticing for the first time that both the chief *and* his witchdoctor were fairly gummy.

'So what happened?'

'He was banished, and imprisoned in the sunken caves beneath the island, the world where only strange fish swim... but he committed an even greater crime while he was interned them. A forbidden pleasure: one of the great sacrificial sins. He took a lover...from below.'

'To be honest, I'd prefer it if we could draw a discreet veil over that bit and take it as read. I'm assuming he was—what— executed?'

Bodiker bowed his head.

'Yes: a necessity. He was sacrificed to the sea gods, along with his forbidden fruit...but the child they had between them was spared and brought into the tribe.'

'You raised that lunatic's *son* as one of your own?'

'We felt we had no choice. The sacrifice provoked great anger among the gods, for we reaped neither fish nor bloodfruit in that terrible year. Besides, the boy was a perfect example of one of our own young, and showed no signs of his father's taint. He must have been biding his time. Now this evil comes among us. This nightmare. This terror. This...'

'...bastard son of a shark and a shapechanging dentist? Terrific news. Just tell me how to get into the caves. We need to end this. Now.'

THROUGH THE FOREST, INTO THE UNDERGROWTH, beneath the giant vine tree, beyond the lowest tier of the tri-level cave system, behind the great stone rock, down the deepest slope of the longest, darkest and dankest tunnel lay a candlelit chamber containing a limpid pool of glimmering green water.

'Seriously—how much further is this place? I thought you imprisoned people here all the time: surely their sentence is served by the time you get them to the front door?'

Bodiker grimaced at the magician, and motioned to the pool.

'Swim below, and you shall find the sacrificial caves...and much good may it do you.'

Blush took a moment to stare balefully at the witchdoctor. Then he removed his robes and all but the most sacred of his undergarments, and dropped into the pool.

A vivid and boldly illuminated world of floating carcasses, severed heads, skeletal limbs and curiously misshapen fish turned slowly all around him as Blush swam through the emerald waters.

When one submerged tunnel bled quickly into another, he began to fear that his hastily gulped oxygen supply would give out before he could reach his destination, but a pool of light suddenly hovered above him and with two determined strokes he broke the surface of the water and clambered onto the rocks of a strikingly beautiful sunken grotto.

There were diametrically beautiful gems encrusted within the walls, two great stone altars wedged together in the centre...and an immediately recognizable tribesman standing at the grotto's only other exit.

The translator half stepped, half staggered forward, sporting two great wounds in his stomach and shoulder.

'You managed to change again then?' Blush smiled, patting his hands quickly on the altar and raising them to conjure a spark of flame. 'I suspect there were barely enough teeth in those two old timers for more than a few hours, though?'

The translator took another step, and flashed a mouthful of long, razor sharp teeth.

'I don't need a few hours to finish *you* off, *wizard*.'

Blush had begun to mutter with grim determination now: in such confined surroundings, he knew he had enough in the concentration tank to bring forth another dramatic burst of fire. Only, *this time* it had to be enough of a gout to get the job done.

'Your father made a terrible mistake down here,' Blush warned, beginning to mutter the start of an incantation. 'You have suffered a cursed life as a result.'

'I agree, wizard...but we all make mistakes.'

The translator lunged forward, grabbing hold of Blush and heaving him into the air. The magician made no attempt to struggle against the attack, but continued to mumble as the heat built between his open palms. The translator charged Blush bodily against the wall, and snatched a rock from an open crevice beside the magician's head.

Raising it up with one arm, the tribesman was easily strong enough to hold Blush against the wall, pinioned helplessly as he aimed the rock directly between the magician's eyes.

The burst of flame was exactly that: a jet of fire that spewed over the translator's head, neck and shoulders, sending the young man staggering backwards with a blood curdling scream of pain. He hit the altar and somersaulted over it to crash land onto the rocks behind, burned horrifically and crawling with ponderous, painstaking effort to the grotto wall.

Blush picked up the rock that had been intended for his head and followed the shapechanger with it. Stalking him slowly and deliberately, he turned the wretched creature onto its back and lifted the rock high above his head.

'We do all make mistakes...but it falls to me to account for your father's.'

The translator looked up at him through sorrowful, bloodshot eyes. 'Then tell me, *wizard*, will you account for all of mine?'

Blush slowly turned to the darkened portal at the far end of the grotto, and discerned the patter of hundreds of tiny feet.

Black Frost

ALICE OLIVIA SCARLETT

THE FIRE WAS CRACKING LOW ON THE HEARTH WHEN then crisp autumn wind carried the sound of hoof beats to the cottage door. I sprang to my feet and grabbed the poker, then crept to the window. I always kept the shutters closed so the cottage would look as uninteresting as possible, but there was a thin gap between the brick wall and the window frame. I placed my eye to the gap and peered out into the night.

At first, nothing. Just the dark of the forest, and the faint swirling October mist rising up from the damp ground.

There—a white blur in the shadows.

A pale horse trotted out of the trees and into the tiny clearing. Utterly beautiful. A small, finely-formed head, long feathers at the fetlocks, and a fire in the way she picked up her hooves. Beautiful. Then I remembered to look at the rider, and was surprised to see that he was also beautiful. Not as beautiful as the horse, obviously, but he had a straight jawline, high cheekbones, a good nose, and his hair under his red feathered cap was dark and curly. I bet that his eyes were dark as well.

He brought the beautiful horse to a halt, and for a moment he sat in the saddle and stared at the cottage. His head was tilted to the side, like a curious bird's, and he was half-smiling. I took his puzzlement as a good sign, and ever so slightly released my death grip on the poker.

There were no saddlebags, and he didn't appear to be armed beyond the knife at his belt. He couldn't have come from far, and he clearly hadn't intended to be out this late. His cloak was trimmed with ermine, but his boots were those fancy knee-high things that I remembered being in fashion when I'd escaped the castle. They were the kind of things young noblemen wore to convince ladies that they were hard-riding, hard-hunting men of the woods rather than the pampered delicate fops they appeared to be.

So, he wasn't looking for me. That was something. But he was still here, and he didn't look as though he were going away. I wondered whether to throw open the door and fling the contents of the chamber pot in his face.

I held my breath as he dismounted and approached the door. He didn't immediately try the latch; instead, he lifted his fist and knocked.

I wasn't entirely sure what to do next. Open the door? But if he wasn't one of the Queen's soldiers come to drag me back to the dungeons, that could only mean one thing.

He was a traveller lost in the woods, seeking a place for the night.

In other words, he was a guest.

I shuddered.

He knocked again. Damn it. So I heaved a great sigh and opened the door.

"Good evening," he began, "I'm terribly sorry for disturbing you, but..." He looked at me properly, and his prepared politeness dribbled away. He blinked. "Um," he said. Then he seemed to shake himself back into propriety. "Um, yes, ah, as I was—I'm very sorry, I know how late it is, but I appear to have lost my way. Both my horse and I would be very grateful if you could share your hospitality for the night."

He had a very pleasant voice, deep and smooth like the black syrupy liquor the Queen had imported from the Indies for her last birthday.

I said, "Alright."

"Alright?"

"Yes. Alright. You can stay the night."

He smiled, and his face was very lovely, sculpted with shadows and the flickering firelight. "Thank you. I must just attend to Caselotti."

I half-closed the door, and glanced around the cottage. I knew it would seem plain to an outsider's eyes, to someone who hadn't seen what it was like when I first arrived here. I had tried to make it beautiful with a spray of golden and orange autumn leaves in an empty green wine bottle on the floor by the hearth, with a string of tiny mouse skulls and soft white dove feathers hanging above my bed, and a cluster of dried rose hips pinned behind the door. But I knew the visitor's fine dark eyes would linger on the rotting floorboards and where the ancient brickwork was crumbling into white dust at the corners.

I tossed a fallen piece of thatch onto the fire. It wasn't my fault if he chose to focus on the dust and age.

He came in after a few minutes, taking off his cap. I could see more clearly now, how the firelight ran over the red velvet pile and golden brocade trim, how it shivered in the white plume and highlighted each barb with golden brilliance.

"Let me take your hat," I said. He gave it to me, and I held it in my hands, feeling how heavy the expensive fabric was.

"So," he said, looking around the room and finally coming back to me with a smile. "I'm Heinrich. Heinrich Baumer." His smile was very wide, and there was a slight hitch in his voice that suggested he was lying.

"Heinrich," I said.

"Yes, that's right."

I put my head on one side and looked at him. I expected his smile to fade and for him to look away, but instead he returned my gaze steadily, and his smile was still very friendly and very charming.

"I don't think that's true," I said.

"Really?" He was teasing.

"No, you're right," I said, "that is a perfectly acceptable alias. Come in, sit down, grace me with your mysterious presence."

"I'm the one with mysterious presence?" He shook his head. "You might dress like a poor cottager, but you don't speak like one. And…" He flushed a little, though his grin didn't waver. "You look too—healthy to have been born to this life."

He was sharper than he looked. Sharper than I'd expected. The old fear flared up inside me, but I caught hold of it like I would a snake and held it at arm's-length. He was not here to kill me or to take me back. That much I was certain of by now; I could tell from the outlines of his too-tight fashionable clothes that the belt-knife was the only weapon he had. And even if he did have other weapons concealed on his person, his manner was wrong. He'd just lost the element of surprise. I knew how the Queen's spies and assassins worked, and beginning a conversation by remarking upon the strangeness of the target's living situation was not the mark of a subtle and therefore successful killer.

"I'm sorry," he said apologetically, losing some of the teasing confidence of a flirtatious noble and instead apparently trying for sincerity. "It's none of my business. I can't barge into your house in the middle of the night and quiz you on your life story. I'm terrible sorry, it was frightfully ill-mannered of me." He gestured toward the fire, at the chair I'd made from fallen tree branches. "Please, sit down. I don't want to disturb you from your normal routine."

I sat down slowly, waiting to see what he would do. He sat down on the hearthstones and crossed his legs like a child waiting for a bedtime story. He held out his hands to the flames.

His spread fingers cut shadows out of the leaping firelight, painting his face black and gold.

I turned his cap in my hands, stroking the soft white feather. "Your horse is called Caselotti," I said.

"Yes, she is."

"She looks like one of the Araby horses."

"Her sire had Araby blood." He sounded pleased. "Are you interested in horses?"

"They're beautiful," I said. The thought of the lovely mare outside warmed me with a quiet happiness.

"But you don't own one. Not out here."

"No."

"Did you have one somewhere else?"

I fixed him with a hard stare. "You're asking a lot of questions."

He grinned. "I know. Sorry. But I'm curious. You're curious."

If I asked why, it would sound like an invitation to continue. I stayed silent. But he told me anyway, leaning forward with his elbows on his knees, smiling up at me through the golden firelight. "A beautiful girl out here all alone in the middle of the forest. You intrigue me."

He waited for me to say something.

Eventually I said, "Sometimes I think the worst thing a man can do is compliment a woman on her beauty. It creates an obligation."

"What do you mean?"

"When a man tells a woman she's beautiful, he sees it as him paying her the highest compliment a man can give. And so he expects similar favours in return."

"You've never heard of compliments just for compliments' sake?"

"Very rarely." Make that never.

"I'm sorry," he said. "I hadn't thought of it that way before."

"Why would you? It's not like it affects you at all."

He half-laughs. "I am sorry, though. I've barged in here, pried into your private affairs, and made you uncomfortable."

"And all that under a false name," I agreed.

He winced. "Yes. That."

"So? What is your name?"

"I'll tell you mine if you tell me yours. A secret for a secret, how about that?"

I grinned. "Done." I slid off the chair onto the floor and linked my hands around my knees. "You first, then."

"Alright. My name is actually Christophe Reizand. My father is the current Baron Reizand."

I had seen his father at court a few times, a very tall, broad man with a booming laugh. I could see the likeness in his son's hooded eyes and thick dark hair. A flash of exhilaration seared through me at having this man here in front of me. A link to the past, bringing it so close I could reach out and touch it.

"Now you," he said. "What's your name?"

"Snow," I said.

He raised an eyebrow quizzically. "Snow?" He looked at my long black hair. "Did you have light hair when you were younger?"

"No, it's always been dark. Maybe it was my mother's way of wishing she had a golden-haired daughter, like in the fairy tales."

"I like dark hair," he said quickly.

"Well, you would," I said, and gestured towards him.

He touched his black curls, grinning ruefully. "Oh yes. I didn't mean that, though."

"I know you didn't," I said. "You meant it as a compliment."

"Well, yes. Sorry. But just as a compliment. Not an obligation."

I stood up and went to the cupboard on the far wall, where I took out the bottle of apple and todberry cordial.

"No, it's fine," he said as I returned to the hearth with two cups. "I don't want to put you to any trouble."

"It's no trouble," I said. I poured out a thin dark stream of the cordial into the cups and handed him one. "Be careful, it's very strong. But it's warming."

He took a careful sip, then raised his eyebrows. He coughed. "That is strong."

"I brewed it myself," I said.

He took another sip. "Mm. Did you carve these cups as well?"

"They were here when I arrived."

"When was that?"

"A while ago."

He grinned. "Do I have to tell you another secret?"

"Yes." I smiled back at him, dipping my head a little so I could see the firelight on my eyelashes. "I like secrets."

"Alright, then." He thought for a bit. "The worst thing I ever did was when I was fifteen. I was in our castle, late at night with some friends, and we all thought it would be hilarious to take a piss in the ornamental fishpond. We all took turns, and the next morning all the fish were dead."

"That's horrible," I said indignantly.

"I know! That's why I said it was the worst thing I'd ever done. I felt awful about it for ages. I still feel awful about it."

"That's good," I said. "Those poor fish."

He held up his hands in mock-surrender. "I know, I know. So come on, then. What's the worst thing you ever did?"

I didn't have to think very hard. "When I was six, I had a governess to teach me my lessons. She was really clever. She seemed to know everything about everything. I remember thinking so clearly, If only I knew everything she did, my lessons would be so much easier. So one night I crept into her room and broke open her skull with the candlestick to eat her brain."

His eyes grew very wide. After a long mute moment, he gave a shaky attempt at a laugh. "I was not expecting you to say that."

"My stepmother was so angry. I think she cried as well. She put the body in the castle sewers, and no one ever found out. But that was the worst thing I ever did, because after that she kept on watching me. She never left me alone, and I was always constantly supervised."

"How dreadful," he said faintly, and swallowed another mouthful of the cordial with a quick, nervous bob of his head.

"You did ask," I say, a little resentfully.

"Yes, yes, I know I did. I just really was not expecting you to say something like that."

"What did you expect? A tale of the day I put on a blue gown instead of a pink one and completely threw off a party's colour scheme? The time I bounced a ball too high and smashed a priceless antique vase?"

"Well, yes."

"I did all those things too," I reassured him. "But those aren't the worst things I've done."

"No. Clearly not." He put the cup down on the floor next to him and rubbed his eyes. "I suppose that's what I get for prying."

"Tell me what the best thing you ever did was," I said.

He avoided eye contact. "Um. I don't know."

"Oh, come on," I said. "You're not playing the game properly."

"Sorry. I think I'm tired."

"Why is your horse called Caselotti?"

"It's just a nice name," he said. His voice sounded thick.

"What does it mean?"

"I don't know."

"I think you should always take care before you name something," I said. "When you name something, you make it real. There's magic in names."

"I'm sorry—pardon?" He blinked and rubbed his face. His hands were slow and clumsy. "Sorry. Sorry…"

I reached over and picked up the cup. I carefully poured the rest of the cordial back into the bottle so not to waste any. He watched with his big dark eyes.

"Your eyes remind me of a cow's," I said to him. "That's not an insult. Cows are beautiful."

"What…" he slurred. He made an ungainly movement forward, as though trying to grab the bottle.

"It's apple," I said to him. "And todberry."

His expression of sleepy confusion changed to one of pure horror. He tried to stand up, but fell back in a sprawl of long limbs. One of his fashionable high boots almost kicked the log out of the fire. He tried to crawl away across the floor, dragging himself on his hands.

I put the cork back in the bottle of cordial. I stepped over him and went back to the cupboard and replaced the bottle. I would have to wash the cup and leave it outside for three days and nights so the elements could cleanse it.

He was moaning, low, deep, without words. But todberry works quickly. He hadn't even reached the door before his strength gave out. I knelt down before him, and saw his pretty dark eyes staring blindly up at me. "Don't worry about Caselotti," I said. "I'll take good care of her."

His body gave one sudden spasm. His heels and his skull thudded against the floor. Then he lay still.

I dragged him outside. A barn owl called close by, and a vixen shrieked into the wind. I took a moment to catch my breath, and then fetched the axe. He had tied Caselotti around the other side, where a rusty trough collected rainwater. I was glad; I didn't want her to see this.

I hauled him away from the cottage and further into the woods. I arranged him on his back, his arms and legs spread out like Leonardo da Vinci's Vitruvian Man, and his head tipped back so his blind eyes stared at the sky and the bright rising moon.

I took a deep breath. "Christophe," I said into the cold night. The name froze in the air, chilled and silver with my breath, and curled away into the darkness. My skin prickled with anticipation. I welcomed it, felt the power flutter like butterflies in my stomach. I had missed this.

"Christophe Reizant." I hefted the axe, and brought it down on his upturned throat. The shock of it jarred all the way up my arms and down my spine. His blood was black and listless, and it stained the leaf litter like thick paint. His neck bones splintered easily. I brought the axe down again, then again until his head was free.

"Christophe Reizant," I said, sending his name up into the air and down into the ground where his blood gleamed like melting obsidian.

I freed his legs and his arms, and divided his torso into two pieces. With each stroke of the axe, I named him and captured his essence, binding him with the dark naming magic that had sent me to my stepmother's dungeons.

Seven pieces, lying amongst the leaves, catching the ground's winter chill.

I struck the axe into the ground a few times to clean it, then went back and fetched the spade. I dug seven holes in the ground, placed each part carefully inside, and then covered them over with the dirt and bloody leaves.

Christophe Reizant. Man that is born of woman hath but a short time to live.

By the time I finished, the sun rising.

I washed off in the water trough. Caselotti snorted when she smelled the blood, and pranced back, pulling at her tether.

"Ssh," I soothed. I extended my hand, and after a few moments of eye rolling and snorting, she warily sniffed my palm. I stroked her mane and the curve of her jaw, and she unbent enough to nibble my hair. I smiled and found her a carrot from the root cellar that she crunched happily.

The cottage was cold but I was too tired to relight the fire, so I simply wrapped myself up in the blankets and went to sleep. My dreams weren't often peaceful, but they were that night, with a faint murmur like a drumbeat hovering behind my sleeping thoughts, and a whisper that might have been the trees chanting the name into the ground.

Christophe Reizant. Christophe Reizant. Christophe Reizant.

I SLEPT ALL THROUGH THE DAY. WHEN I WOKE, IT WAS dark, past midnight. My face was very cold, so I burrowed down in the bed and closed my eyes again.

I slept for a little while longer before I was woken by a knock at the door. I lay still for a few moments, preparing myself, before I got out of bed and padded to the door.

Outside were seven small men. They were naked, but caked with dirt and orange and yellow and black-spotted leaves. Their eyes gleamed very white in their muddy faces.

I smiled at them all. "Hello."

"Snow White," one of them said. His voice was rich and deep, and his hair, like all the others', was thick and dark and curly.

"Do you want to come in?" I said, and held the door open as they marched, single-file, into the cottage.

Laid Bare

KIRSTY LOUISE FARLEY

I WALKED THROUGH THE FOREST AND SAW YOUR FACE in the trees. It followed me even though I asked it not to. I hid for days in places I thought you could not find me, but you always did. That's when I started to really see who you were, you were the blood in my veins, the voice in my head and the bastard who wouldn't let me go. Your face became more haunting within the distorted trees, whose leaves and branches would cross over so quickly that I would always lose sight of you. Crowding me, even in darkness, I had to remove you from me. So I cut you out slowly with knives I made myself. My Kidney. My Appendix. My Heart. Each organ at a time until I lay amongst the foliage. You bled out of me and I was finally allowed to go home. I lay there for days with a smile on my face. Crows sat upon me, gathering their friends, picking at what was left of you within me. It never did hurt too much, it was probably the excitement of the whole ordeal being over.

Gradually the winds became more frequent and aggressive, forcing the trees to abandon their leaves that passed over me like pixies venturing into the night on wild stallions. I was left with lank wooden fingers hanging over me while they creaked lullabies throughout the night. Each day I was encased by the leaves who were not able to flee so quickly. They started to rot below me and I could feel my bed become softer as my half-rotten corpse sunk into theirs. I was picked at by any passer-by that would have me, they enjoyed my cold flesh and muscle ripping between their teeth. However, as the leaves rotted below me more frequently and the lank wooden fingers remained, each creature seemed to go someplace else. Finally the occasional morning song that the darkling thrush could not seem to resist only ever greeted me. His curious eyes flicked light upon me as his tiny feet clicked over my bones while he sang and danced only for me. One bitterly cold morning, as the sun crept through the lowest points of the trees, snow began to fall. As I noticed the soft flakes fall from the sky the bitter cold seemed to warm itself with a welcoming expression. It placed itself upon my bones more gently than you ever kissed my lips. That was when I realised…I am loved. In this moment I am shrunken, hollow and cold, but a moistened angel falling upon me so delicately lets me know that I am loved. Intimately we lay together, sacred and forever. Until one day a child fell around my legs to uncover my bones. Screaming to his parents, "Something horrible is over there." I was shocked.

After all, I created such a masterpiece out of the broken body you left behind. I had given myself to the ground while it encased me as I healed and eventually it turned me into an expressionless trail of cold, rough and dusty bones. The animals even seemed to admire me so much that they left me to display myself as I wanted, while it was only the birds who entertained me. Now I was being degraded by three sets of wide eyes and open jaws.

"It's definitely human," she said… "Don't look darling!"

The child hid in his mother's coat.

"I'm going to call the police," said the man.

The woman used her hand to shield her child's face even more so than her coat did as she looked down at me. Her expression was fixed upon where mine did not appear. Her mouth wider than the vastest of landscapes, her eyes glazed with such fear that I could barely see her pupils and her chest rising and falling more rapidly than the winter's rough tide. She did not move from this stance until her husband returned from making the call. As he appeared from the milky darkness that the sunset had begun to create I knew that my time here was over.

That night was the darkest night I had ever experienced in the forest. If the blackness could have folded into itself and out again not a single thing would have flinched. Such an extraordinary sight. I lay in silence trying to preserve every feeling the place gave me. Feeling the rotting foliage beneath me I took in the way it pressed against my cold bones to almost warm them against the cold winds which blew through the trees. Each time they creaked me a lullaby and let their branches move so swiftly that they could have been dancing too. I had not seen a creature for a long while among the area which I lay but that night I heard all kinds of paws running around me to eventually settle. Squeaks and whines came from the creatures who seemed to sit around me in a circle and that's when I heard the wings of many birds break the air with an elegant urgency. Resting upon the branches on the trees they chirped and squawked. All the while I could hear my darkling thrush among them who seemed to be singing the most melancholy song that had ever graced my presence. I don't know how long they sung to me for but I wanted to be able to do something in order to make myself stay.

As the sun rose I saw the snow almost pour into my bones as it melted so rapidly. I almost felt it run away from me. Sun rays lit them up so delightfully that they seemed to glow, but this morning they only exposed me to the officers arriving at the scene. I was interrogated by their latex covered fingers and could not do a single thing as they all stood around me, discussing what might have happened. Not a single one of them considered how I would feel about them carelessly moving me about like I was something to work out. I could not work out why, if the animals knew why I was there, they could not see it also. One of them derived that it was homicide. My masterpiece, my creation… Slowly, they began to take me apart. I had spent so long putting myself back together and they could not see what I had created. I began to think it was because they did not see what you had done to me. How you tore me apart from flesh, to muscle and bone while all I did was get lost in the fucked-up optimism that came from desperation. They did not see how I laid myself here to escape the vulgar way you picked at my brain with your cast iron teeth and the way you followed me through every sunlit garden I ever tried to hide in. So eventually each part of me sat in a separate bag piled one upon another inside a case marked 'evidence.'

Gently, at least, they laid me out on a metal table and this time I really did feel the cold pierce through my bones. I saw them try to put me back together, but it wasn't the same... They did not see that I was magnificent in the way I had fallen. I was left with a woman whose latex hands inspected me again and again. Routinely she cleaned my bones and soaked them in bleach, which made them look so delicate and pure, almost sickly. Dried out, she took one of my bones. Not a single bit of fat remained and as she carved into it I saw the last fire burn out.

"I can't find anything on the system," she said aloud.

I tried to reach out to myself but I could not touch a single thing. I did not know where I was going to end up but all I knew was that I had been taken apart again. Helpless I lay there for a few more hours until somebody came, with their latex hands, to bag me up and pile me on top of myself inside that same case. I think it was some kind of evidence vault that I was put into. I am not so sure, but I've been here for a while now. I do not have any part of nature here to comfort me, animals do not admire me so much that they leave me the way I fell and my darkling thrush is no longer here to entertain me. I am bleached and dried, hauled up in a silent darkened vault with no one to admire me. Each day I take myself back to the place where I laid so beautifully. Delicately wonderful upon the dying leaves, protected from you by the lank wooden fingers overhanging from the trees and admired by every creature who wishes to pass me. I see my darkling thrush waiting for me, his eyes twitching with light exposing his melancholy wondering. He only sings when the sun rises now... When the milky blue of the morning still lets him think that I may be laid bare where I once was.

Life and Times of a Zombie

MATTHEW MUNSON

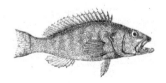

THE DAY I DIED, I WAS IN THE SUPERMARKET.

Becky and I were doing the weekly shop at the time. The twins were in their pram, laughing and gurgling away as nine-month-old babies often do. Becky and I were in the sauces aisle talking about mayonnaise, of all things. It's weird how the mind remembers the silly details. I still can't remember the colour of my wife's eyes, but I can remember that we were arguing about mayonnaise.

"I don't see why you're so fussed about buying a brand," I said to her. "Mayo is mayo."

"The own-brand stuff tastes cheap."

I couldn't argue; it tasted cheap because it was cheap. But cheap was good; with Robert and Sarah in our lives, and me being the only breadwinner, as far as I was concerned we could do with a few more own-brand products.

"Becky, it's not as if—"

I gasped as a shaft of pain shot up the base of my neck and into my head. It felt like a poker had stabbed into of my brain. My hand shot round to feel what had happened. There was nothing there.

"Babe?" Becky asked, her face screwed up with concern. "What's wrong?"

My eyes rolled up in my head...and I died, right there in the supermarket.

ATHEISTS HAVE ALWAYS SAID THAT WHEN YOU'RE DEAD, you're dead. Nothing more, nothing less. I wasn't bothered about life after death; after all, if the atheists were right, I wouldn't know about it anyway.

Turns out there is life after death. It just wasn't what I expected. My life after death began about eight hours after I died.

I was in a dark tube and was bloody cold. There was no way I could sit up; while the tube was about eight feet long, it was barely a foot in height. I couldn't imagine the designers of these tubes expecting many people to wake up from death.

I could hear the muffled voices of two people outside the tube; I felt a sudden surge of anger well up inside me at their freedom. They were out there, and I was stuck in this stupid, sodding box.

With some difficulty, I managed to turn onto my stomach and saw a small door in front of me. It was securely locked—from the outside—with no key or handle for me to grab.

"Hey!" I yelled. "Can anyone hear me? You've made a mistake, I'm still alive!"

I listened carefully, but the two voices had fallen silent. For a brief second, I felt scared…and alone. Those feelings were quickly replaced by something else; it was anger, a deep, bubbling anger that started in the pit of my stomach and then blossomed to my chest and throat. I felt my fists clenching and my teeth ground together as the anger throbbed through my body.

I had never really been an angry person. I liked to think of myself as being quite laid-back, so this anger coursing through my veins was a new sensation.

It felt good.

My left fist lashed out and smashed against the door. It ploughed through the hard, cold metal like paper and I instantly felt the warmth of the room beyond.

The room looked like all the morgues I'd seen on TV shows; cold and clinical, with a couple of tables and various pieces of equipment—knives and things—dotted around. A man and a woman were stood in the middle of the room. They were staring at me in shock.

I felt invincible.

My teeth plunged into the old man's neck and ripped away a chunk of his flesh. I barely registered his cry of pain as I felt his blood splatter across my face and down my throat. I roared with pleasure as the taste of his blood and flesh hit my taste buds; it made me feel alive and satiated my hunger, at least for a moment. For that brief, pleasurable moment, I felt whole.

I watched the old man's body drop; he was dead before he hit the floor. I immediately knew it was a good thing that he hadn't fought back or ran away. It meant I could enjoy my food without having to waste time chasing after him first.

The hunger was still there, gnawing away at me and urging me on. I glanced down at the old man, his body still intact and ready for me to feast on.

I knelt down beside him and began to eat.

I WAS CONSCIOUS AGAIN. I WAS ME. I FELT WEAK, ALL of a sudden, and my legs were shaking.

Three corpses were on the floor, ripped to shreds. Limbs were torn from torsos and heads from necks. There was the smell of death and blood everywhere. Two of the corpses were the man and woman I had seen when I punched through the door; they must have been doctors, judging by the white coats...or what was left of the coats. The third person—a man—had some sort of uniform on.

Was he a security guard? I wondered.

It took me a moment to realise that I wasn't upset by what I could see. In fact, all it was doing was making me hungry. I froze for a moment, almost intoxicated by the sight of the fresh meat in front of me. I could feel my mouth drooling at the site of so much blood and flesh. I was thrown by the sudden craving and needed to get away from it, to give me time to think.

There was a set of automatic doors to my right, although

they didn't open as I approached them. A sudden surge of anger flooded through me and the doors folded in on themselves under my fists.

"What the hell...?"

I stared at the doors, trying to figure out what I had done to make them cave so easily. Gingerly, I reached out and touched a piece of the door. It was folded back on itself, showing the corridor beyond. It felt like metal—cold and smooth—and looked like metal.

Metal it is then. So how did I manage to punch through it?

I looked over my shoulder. If I can punch through doors, I could kill someone without breaking a sweat.

As I looked over the carnage, that same deep, feral hunger started to gnaw away at me again. I turned away and tried to focus on an exit. Accepting that I seemed to have developed new strengths, I stretched the doors wide enough apart to let me through. As I stepped through, I looked left and right, but each curved end was empty.

I'd usually feel nervous when I was an unfamiliar place; apologetic, even. Becky would always get annoyed at me, but I couldn't help it; it was just me. Now, however, I felt different. I felt more assured and confident.

I began walking down the corridor to look for anyone. I passed a few side rooms, but they were either locked or empty. As I rounded the corridor, I came across a laundry cupboard, its contents spilling out over the floor. Seeing pyjamas amongst the laundry made me realise, for the first time, that I was naked.

No-one needs to see that.

After I'd dressed in some doctor's scrubs, I walked to the nearby lift and pressed the call button; it 'pinged' immediately and the doors opened.

Abruptly, I was on my back, feeling the tiled floor slamming into my shoulder blades. I called out in shock; that had hurt. My head snapped up and I was confronted by a snarling, angry face directly in mine.

I was battered by my attacker's arms, and I suspect that I would have been bitten if my hands, placed firmly against her growling throat, weren't keeping those teeth away from me.

I strained against her arms, but she was at least as strong as me. I thought back to the morgue and how I had managed to destroy the doors without any apparent effort.

My god, she's like me! I thought with sudden exhilaration. *Maybe she knows what's going on!*

She seemed to realise that in the same moment, and the attack stopped. Her face changed and became calmer.

I pushed myself off the floor as she climbed off me.

"Sorry about that," she said. "I didn't realise you were one of us."

'One of us?' I thought. What does that mean?

Despite her aggression, I knew—somehow—that I could trust her, and she seemed to think the same of me. The rage... the anger...in her face had been total and awesome, and I found myself wondering if I had looked like that to the people back in the mortuary.

"What's your name?"

I blinked. "Sorry?"

"What were you thinking about?"

"I was wondering what's happening to me…us," I replied. "I feel different…and my name's Ryan."

"Mine's Alexandra, but I'll break your legs if you call me that. Alex will do."

"Do you know what's happening?"

"Not a clue, my friend." She smiled. "I don't think that's what you wanted to hear, was it?"

"How did you guess?"

"I was a psychologist before it happened."

I raised an eyebrow. "Before what happened?"

"Before I died," she replied.

I found myself struggling to understand what she was saying.

"You're dead?"

Alex nodded. "We both are."

WE'D GONE OUTSIDE TO THE CAR PARK. I HADN'T WANTED to stay inside the morgue as I'd contemplated the subject of death.

"I'm dead?"

Alex turned to face me. "Yes. You're also stronger, fitter and more confident than you were before."

"Stronger..." I muttered. "Yeah, I've already encountered that. It felt...good."

"We're beyond human."

As soon as Alex said the word human, I tensed. Bile blocked the back of my throat for a moment and I growled. My eyes darted around the silent car park, checking for any invaders.

"What's wrong with me?" I breathed. "Why do I get so angry when I think of..."

I couldn't finish the sentence, as the bile started to rise again in my throat; I opened and closed my mouth a few times, but no words could come out. I looked at Alex, needing answers; the smile had vanished from her face and replaced by understanding.

"What's wrong with me?" I asked.

"Nothing's wrong with you," she replied. "You're more alive now than you were, ironically. Your body knows what it wants. It doesn't like the living...they feel wrong. All the emotions that clogged up your thinking are gone. You're free."

I was silent for a while, trying to absorb what Alex was telling me. It had taken me longer to wake up than the others, having been slowed by the coldness in the morgue, so Alex knew more than I did. I couldn't deny what she was saying, though; I did feel stronger, better, more powerful than I had done before...and unencumbered by worry or doubt. A thought suddenly occurred to me.

"My wife," I said. "My children. Where are they?"

"They're probably still human. They're not us."

The bile flooded back and I screamed with rage. I hated humans and they needed to die – all of them. I no longer cared who I hurt. My hunger returned, and there was only one thing that could satiate me; human flesh.

Alex smiled as she saw the change in my eyes.

"You're free," she said. "Welcome to the new dawn."

ALEX AND I STAYED TOGETHER FOR FOUR MONTHS, hunting humans for the meat and the sport. Some put up a good fight, but others just cowered. They acted like nothing more than sheep—frightened, terrified sheep running from wolves.

However, even sheep could sometimes fight back when in a pack. We had hunted a herd of weak, defenceless humans to a barn where they were cowering from us like the afore-mentioned sheep going to the slaughter.

I could feel my mouth drooling as I heard them barring the doors. We climbed the side of the building silently and quickly; our reflexes having been expanded along with our strength. It was easy to find tiny hand-holds along the wooden slats of the building. We were soon on the roof and stood over the skylight.

Alex looked at me. "Ready?"

I licked my lips, ravenously hungry now. "Do you even have to ask?"

She kicked in the skylight. I immediately heard screams from below; they'd clearly forgotten about that.

Idiots.

I jumped through and landed on the muddy ground. Thirty or so villagers were cowering at one end of the long barn; they were a mixture of adults, old people and children.

Oh yes, I was going to feast here.

One of the older men charged forward with a scythe, ready to attack. I deftly stepped to one side and pushed him to the ground. His arms—and the scythe—flailed as he fell. Out of the corner of my eye, I saw Alex drop through the skylight and land on the ground…but didn't get up again.

I caught the look of stunned shock on the old man's face as he lay there on the floor. His scythe suddenly had a film of blood covering it. It wasn't until I looked round did I realise what had happened. Alex had dropped through the skylight just as the old man had started falling—and his scythe had cut her head clean off.

She was gone. Just like that.

I felt numb with shock. She had been my ally, my sidekick for the past four months. We had fought, killed and feasted together. We were the undead—we weren't meant to die again. We were meant to live forever.

Rage surged through my body and I roared with fury. The old man looked terrified and tried to crawl back, pushing himself as far away as possible from me as I lunged for him. I missed his leg by an inch and I stepped forward to try again when—

"Hey!"

I looked over my shoulder. A woman, in her twenties, had called out to me. She didn't look scared; she looked determined.

"Why don't you pick on someone your own size?" she shouted.

"You wouldn't want to fight me, little girl," I growled. "I will feast on your liver for breakfast." A grin formed on my lips. "Wait your turn."

The woman took a step forwards. "I think it's your turn now."

I looked behind her. Suddenly, the group of villagers weren't acting like frightened sheep; they were stood together, shoulder to shoulder, and they all look angry. They had seen Alex die. They now knew that the undead could die again—and stay dead.

Things had taken an unexpected turn. I managed to push down the rage that was consuming me and use my head. I couldn't fight off thirty villagers determined to hurt me, not without doing some serious damage to my body. And I don't heal anymore.

For the first time in my death, I had to run. I had to leave fresh meat behind and escape. I climbed up the wall and pulled myself through the skylight. While they were still pulling the furniture away from the doors, I was already deep into the forest.

Two days had passed. I remained hidden deep in the forests of the Scottish Highlands. Occasionally, I would come across a solitary human. I fed on them.

On the third day, I saw a black helicopter flying overhead. I watched it circle round for a moment and then release a cloud of coloured gas from pumps in its tail end.

I can't escape it, I realised. *Even if I run, I'll still breathe it in. Damn. This is how I'm going to die.*

Calmly, I sat down on the ground, leaned against a mighty oak tree—and closed my eyes. If I was going to die, I was going to die with dignity.

THE APOCALYPSE HAD ENDED THAT DAY.

A group of scientists, working under heavily armed guard somewhere in Kent, had found the genetic marker behind my death and rebirth. Their vaccine mitigated its effects; it removed our hunger and gave us back our emotions.

It was a cruel vaccine. I wish it had killed me outright. Instead, it had given me back my life, without actually giving me back my life. I was practically human again.

All I could think about was my family. Were Becky and the twins safe? Were they even still alive? Were they still human? I hadn't thought about them in four months; I hadn't had any need to, after all. I had loved my new world.

Now that my hunger had gone, I remembered what my life had been like before my death. I loved my family, and I wanted them back. I wanted to go back to my old life; I wanted to kiss my kids goodnight and argue about mayonnaise with Becky.

I started the long walk home.

I LOST TRACK OF TIME. IT MUST HAVE BEEN MONTHS, but I didn't know how long. I was walking from the Scottish Highlands to the southern tip of Kent, and it was taking forever.

Eventually, after so many months of walking, the scenery started to become more familiar. This started to give me flashbacks to my old life; driving to my parents' house, out here in the suburbs, or going to the out-of-town shopping centre…or just going out for a drive with Becky, back when we were dating.

I'm nearly home, I realised. *I'm so close.*

"Evening!"

I was startled out of my reverie by a cheerful voice from behind me. I checked that my hood was still in place—it was—and turned around.

A middle-aged man was walking across the green; a Jack Russell was on a lead at his feet, looking desperate for its freedom.

I knew how it felt.

"E-evening," I replied.

I was terrified of being discovered. I couldn't risk it. As the Jack Russell darted off across the green, I turned to go.

"Are you new to the village?" the man asked.

"Erm, no, I'm…just a visitor. I'm passing through."

In the rapidly-fading light, I saw the man nod. He walked towards me, and my stomach did a back flip. Quickly adjusting my hood, so that it covered as much of my face as possible, I took a step back.

"A lot of people do," the man said. "Visit, I mean. It's a nice little village—always has been, despite the recent… problems."

Oh god, he knows. I started to panic, and wished I could still control my emotions like I had done when—*No, don't! You don't want to go back to…then!*

The man stopped in front of me and peered after his dog.

"I can't see Henry," he said, peering into the gloom. "Can you?"

I shook my head. I didn't trust my voice not to quaver with fear, so stayed silent.

"It was a terrible time, wasn't it," he said abruptly. "All those dead people, hunting and killing everyone. We lost… well, we lost more than we should have."

I was glad I had hidden my white, dead hands in my jeans; I didn't want to get recognised, not when I was so close to home.

"Yeah," I replied. "No one was safe."

"Did you lose anyone?"

"What? I—oh, er, yes. I lost my wife and two children."

I immediately hated myself for the lie, but it was said now—I couldn't change it.

"I lost my brother and his wife," he replied. "They were butchered, just over there by the post office. I didn't see it happen, thankfully."

I heard the Jack Russell barking excitedly in the distance and found myself wishing I could be that carefree. Abruptly, the man stuck out a hand.

"Samuel Hiller," he said. "Pleasure to meet you, Mr…?"

I felt another surge of panic; the second I put my hand in his, he would know what I was. The clamminess of my skin and the missing finger were giveaways.

I just want my family back, I thought. *Please don't do this to me!*

I was saved by Henry. He came bounding back across the green, still full of energy and excitement. He barrelled into my legs, righted himself and began weaving in between our legs.

I laughed at the dog, so full of energy and happy to be back near his owner. I knelt down but, as soon as I stroked him, however, he yelped and jumped back.

"Henry?" Hiller said. "What's wrong with you, you silly boy?"

He knelt down and grabbed hold of Henry, stroking him to stop the little dog from shaking.

"Sorry about that," he said. "I don't know what's got into him. He's normally—"

I instantly knew why he had stopped. Stood opposite Samuel, my hands were visible. Pale white with occasional purple patches showed up even in the darkness of the evening. The ring finger on my right hand was also gone.

Henry, emboldened by being in his owner's arms, started to growl.

"You're an abomination!" Samuel hissed. "You don't belong here!"

"I don't belong anywhere!" I exclaimed. "I just want to go home!"

Samuel scoffed. "Your home's a cemetery. You belong in hell!"

"Please don't tell anyone!" I begged. "Please...let me leave. I don't mean you any harm. I just want to find my family."

"Why shouldn't I call for the authorities?" Samuel demanded. "You deserve to be exterminated!"

I flinched at the word exterminated; it sounded so harsh and final.

"Please..." I pleaded. "Please, let me go. I'm heading for Dover to find my family. I don't want to hurt anyone. The cure saved me of all that hate."

"Dover?" he repeated. "You're going to Dover?"

I nodded. "That's where I lived before...well, before all this happened. I'm looking for my family."

Samuel blinked, and hugged Henry close to his chest.

"You...you haven't heard?" There was a quaver in his voice. His fear seemed momentarily forgotten.

"If you haven't noticed, I'm a goddamn zombie, Samuel! I don't really keep up with the news!"

Samuel took a step back, his fear showing again.

"Look, I'm sorry," I said, holding my hands up placatingly. My voice quavered with emotion as I went on; "I'm just tired. I want to see my family again."

"I don't think you'll find them."

"What do you mean?" My head started throbbing. "What's happened?"

"Dover was hit badly by the virus," he said. "Over two-thirds of the population became zombies. Some moved out the area, to find...fresh meat elsewhere, I assume. But a lot stayed."

"I know," I whispered. "I was one of those that left."

"The government couldn't control them all," Samuel went on. "The army were overwhelmed; there were just too many of them. So they scorched the town."

My knees buckled and I fell to the ground. The earth and grass were hard beneath my knees but I didn't care.

"They...scorched..." I tried to process what Samuel had said, but I couldn't. "No...they can't...my family..."

Samuel's eyes had filled with tears. He nodded. "No one survived. The zombies fried. Anyone trying to leave the town's boundaries was shot on site, human or zombie. They couldn't tell who was who. I'm so sorry."

I barely heard what Samuel was saying. All I could see, in front of my eyes, were my children screaming as the flames consumed them...held by my burning wife.

My throat burned as I screamed with grief. I didn't care who heard me. I wanted to die. But I was already dead. I had a half-life, and I wanted it to end.

"Kill me," I begged. "Burn me. Let me die and be with my family."

Thanephant: An Elephantasy

JANET GOGERTY

JOSH LOOKED AT THE BLACK AND WHITE PHOTOS THAT explained why this Wetherspoons pub boasted such a name. He smiled to himself, he had arrived at Margate railway station only fifteen minutes ago and already he had his new big idea. He looked at his phone, his friends would be here in ten minutes. When Dan and Natalie emailed You must come down, they probably imagined him staying for a weekend to admire their rescued Victorian villa.

'Hey Josh, long time no see,' said Dan.

'What's with the wheelie suitcase?' said Natalie. 'You haven't thrown out the old rucksack at last?'

'New suitcase, new rucksack, new life,' said Josh. 'I'm going to be an entrepreneur, you did say Margate was where it was all happening?'

Dan and Natalie squeezed past the suitcase, dodged an escaped toddler and sat down with their friend.

'Well...for arty types and property developers...we'll be commuting up to London for the foreseeable future,' said Natalie. 'Me at least, until I start my maternity leave.'

This clue to their latest news was missed by Josh, whose

head was still in the entrepreneurial clouds.

'You haven't actually given up your job, have you?' said Dan.

'Which one? There have been a few since you last saw me. Anyway, what are you eating and drinking, my treat, the least I can do…lemonade Natalie, that's not like you? We're supposed to be celebrating.'

While Josh was at the bar ordering, Natalie and Dan looked at each other and the large suitcase. Josh was the antidote to some of the more boring friends in their eclectic group so they had no idea what to expect from the weekend.

'So did you say you have a sea view?'

'Not exactly, unless you climb on the chimney pot, but we're quite close to everything: the beach, Dreamland, Turner Gallery.'

After their meal they strolled across the road to see low tide sunset on the beach, then past the Turner Contemporary and along to the end of the harbour wall. Josh knew he was going to love it here.

'You still haven't told us your big idea,' said Natalie.

'A jumbo idea inspired by Wetherspoons, haven't you guessed?'

'You want to open a pub?' said Dan.

'Nope, been there done that, we've just been sitting in The Mechanical Elephant…'

'Yes, but what idea did that give you?' asked Natalie.

'The return of the Mechanical Elephant, a robotic pachyderm

for the Twenty First Century, an animatronic mammoth for Margate.'

'Is someone going to do that?' said Natalie.

'Yes, me.'

'How come no one else has had the idea, no one at Dreamland...I don't think I've heard or read of anyone suggesting it,' said Dan. 'Too expensive no doubt.'

'Have you inherited some money?' asked Natalie.

'I should be so lucky...'

'...and you always said technology was the only GCSE you failed...' added Dan.

'You're missing the point here,' grinned Josh, 'entrepreneurs neither pay nor make, they just come up with the ideas.'

On the walk back home Josh elaborated on his plans. 'Win–win situation, I get local historians interested. I mean, what happened to the original elephant?'

'How long ago are we talking about?' said Natalie.

'1949, the fifties.'

'That is a long time ago, poor old Jumbo long ago rusted away on a scrap heap,' Dan laughed, 'and the idea obviously didn't catch on.'

'But it will now; no animal welfare problems like donkeys on the beach so animal charities interested, drawing attention to the plight of real elephants, conservationists keen. Probably have to have seat belts on the howdah these days. Wetherspoons are bound to invest.'

'Aren't they only interested in buying more pubs?' said Dan.

'The money I spend in Wetherspoons I think they would happily divert some of their profits to me. Dreamland and the council should also be interested.'

'…and big boys who love toys,' said Natalie. 'Men who've got more money than sense, perhaps it could work?'

Josh was taken aback with the house and the work his friends had taken on; from his brief experience of property development it was obvious they would have no money to invest in his project, but the house was so big he was unlikely to get in their way. The kitchen was larger than the flat he had just given up and Dan, a keen cook, proudly showed all the new kitchen gadgets they had never had room for before. Josh looked forward to some good meals.

Dan and Natalie thought Josh would be impressed with the historical research they had done on their house and the proposed games room in the cellar, but he was far more interested in the history of petrol driven elephants.

The young couple went up to St. Pancras each morning and returned each evening to be greeted by more elephant news and contacts made. Josh seemed to have everything sorted except where the elephant would be made and from what. The council promised grants if local schools were involved. An artist, who specialised in covering large items in swathes of patchwork fabric, was getting an Arts Council grant if she got community groups involved; a call had gone out to scour charity shops for grey fabrics. Knit and natter groups pledged to knit a blanket fit for a royal elephant. But Josh still had to find a group of mad scientists.

Somehow he fixed an appearance on News South East, followed by a slot on The One Show in which he pleaded for the need to get children interested in science. Cue for pictures of cute Margate infant school children with papier-mâché elephants and mammoth murals.

Meanwhile, Natalie and Dan's online food shopping bill was growing and so was Natalie's stomach. Their home was stashed with furniture and stuff well-meaning relatives had given them, now baby paraphernalia was beginning to appear. The sitting room, artistically decorated by Natalie, was the only haven of calm. There was no sign of Josh finding a place of his own to rent, even though they pointedly referred to the room where he slept as the spare room and refused to move any junk out of it. The future nursery had become an operations room for project pachyderm, with drawings of mechanical skeletons instead of cute teddies on the walls. Josh assured them of their share in the profits from the jumbo enterprise.

Mutual friends came down from London and elsewhere, keen to see what they were crowd-funding. Natalie and Dan were equally keen for Josh to succeed, they could not contemplate the consequences of failure.

The construction work was top secret, the scientists and mechanics anonymous. No one knew what was going on in an empty hangar under 24-hour guard at the closed Manston Airport.

Josh made another appearance on News South East explaining how the huge tusks would be made from recycled plastic bottles.

'But how is the elephant actually going to work?' asked the presenter.

'That must remain a secret until after the test run, but I can announce the winner of the schools' competition to name the elephant.'

A shy child edged into camera view and after some Oscar-style drama turned a huge card towards the camera. THANEPHANT.

'Oh,' twittered the presenter, 'is that a boy or a girl's name?'

'It's non…b…byrony,' stuttered the child.

'The elephant is non-binary,' corrected Josh. 'Genderless, makes things easier.'

The hangar doors opened to reveal Thanephant in all its glory. The huge ears flapped and it lifted its head to show off the long curving tusks adorned with flowers made by the children. When the animatronic mammoth trumpeted triumphantly, windows a mile away vibrated and locals called the police. It was the proudest moment of Josh's life and he shook hands with the six creators. Like a child with a new toy he urged them to demonstrate a few steps. Scientist A touched the screen of his state-of-the-art iPad; a huge foot lifted and returned to the ground. Thanephant took a few paces, faster than they anticipated. The controller hurriedly swiped the screen and Thanephant stood motionless.

'Ladies and Gentlemen, we've done it!' said Josh. 'Now to get Big T to the seafront. A low loader is not the style for such a magnificent beast, it should walk there!'

'But we have to do the test run first,' said Scientist B.

'Of course,' said Josh. 'A test run to the sea front will gain the publicity we need, but can it walk that far, how many miles before its batteries need recharging?'

'Thanephant is one hundred percent solar powered; if it's a sunny day he could walk hundreds of miles.'

'Can it find the way?'

'It has next generation sat-nav.'

Team Thanephant were enthralled as they furtively put the creature through its paces round the back of the hangar; the whole was so much greater than the sum of the parts, physically and figuratively.

Saturday Test Day came. The team had reluctantly agreed with Josh that telling the authorities would spoil the surprise element and lead to red tape; he had assured them that no licence or MOT was needed. They were of one accord that Scientist A would be the mahout and Josh would be among the four passengers for the maiden voyage. The creature moved obediently to the mounting block. Josh had never met a real elephant and was not sure how large a fully grown one would be, but now he was up close up, Thanephant was far bigger than the creature he had imagined. They all clambered inelegantly onto the howdah.

In hindsight, Scientist A realised he should not have programmed the most direct route into the sat-nav. Luckily there were few observers around to see Thanephant trampling over the cabbage fields, but as they approached the town and the mahout accidentally swiped sound effects on the iPad screen, people began to come out of their houses and stop their cars. From a distance Thanephant looked real. A police helicopter appeared overhead.

Josh tweeted Kent Police to reassure them, but suggested crowd control might be needed. Now seemed a good moment to tweet all the supporters of the project; by the time they reached the sea front, crowd control was definitely needed.

At the Turner Contemporary, Natalie and Dan sat in the cafe enjoying the view of the sunny harbour and Josh-free-time to discuss Natalie's birth plan.

'Is there something on today? Looks very busy out there,' said Dan.

'What's that just in the distance, near Wetherspoons?'

A huge graceful shape, like a ship in full sail, colours glinting in the sunlight. Suddenly a prehistoric roar made the windows shudder and the customers jump up in alarm. Outside, the crowds seemed to roll in waves.

'Oh God, he's done it.' Natalie knocked the coffee off the table of the next customer as she struggled to rise up out of her seat.

Some customers rushed outside, while others fled for the inner sanctuary of the gallery. Dan urged Natalie to stay inside, but she did not intend to miss the spectacle, which was still safely in the distance.

Horns were beeping, police sirens wailing, and an old man turned to them.

'He's come back, I knew he would, and this time he's real.'

Josh had planned that the procession would halt outside The Mechanical Elephant, where excited customers and staff were already crowding the balcony for a better view. It was at that moment that Scientist A, already feeling very queasy, having not factored in the possibility of motion sickness, dropped his iPad. A helpful member of the public picked it up, but the mahout was far too high for him to hand it back and Scientist A could only climb down if Thanephant halted. The iPad was designed to only respond to the fingerprint touch of Scientist A and he had accidentally swiped speed increase as he tried to save it. The four legs were gathering pace. The passer-by handed it to a policeman. Crowd control was no longer needed; the crowds were fleeing, but those on the beach looked up in alarm. Thanephant's engineering was well-designed and it descended the harbour steps gracefully, with only one passenger falling off. Josh clung on with a mixture of terror and exhilaration. It was low tide, the sand slowed Thanephant down only a little.

'What's plan B?' Josh asked the mahout. 'This would be a good place to stop.'

They crossed the beach and had nearly reached the end of the harbour wall, and were aware of a police car racing along the harbour arm. As they passed the end of the harbour wall the policeman was frantically waving the iPad, then started to climb down the ladder.

Thanephant waded on, undeterred. The team were relieved to

see a lifeboat out at sea, but the crew's loud hailer was drowned out by frantic trumpeting. Those on board Thanephant—strange how Josh was already thinking in maritime terms—were dismayed to see the lifeboat heading inland while they were heading out to sea. They should try to swim to shore before it was too late, but Josh knew they must not desert a sinking elephant.

The tide was too low for the lifeboat to make direct contact with the policeman. The officer, faced with an iPad screen that would not respond, wondered if he could do something useful with a long rope and waterproof bag.

The skipper of the lifeboat hoped he had understood the policeman's radio message correctly: the strange mechanical elephant was heading further out and the tide was coming in. The bag landed in the water, but they hooked it out and were soon alongside the Thanephant. The sea lapped at the feet of those on the howdah and was round the waist of the mahout. Crowds had now gathered on the harbour wall, figuring that the safest place to be and a good spot to observe the strange scene. The bag was passed up to the mahout; shakily he took the iPad out and within seconds Thanephant halted. The lifeboat crew urged everyone to clamber on board the boat, when two of them were safe Josh reached out his arm to stop Scientist A sliding down.

'No, we must ride back in triumph to the beach. This publicity is fantastic! Thanephant, the Amphibious Anima-tronic Mammoth of Margate!'

Lucy

SARAH TAIT

I PAY A MINDER SO THAT I CAN WORK. I KNOW LOTS of people disapprove of my choice, and think I should be at home with her all day. 'Now is when she needs you most.'—I see their eyes accuse. But I love my job, and I loved my life the way it was. I didn't plan on having Lucy. So now I've got this woman in—Brenda. As soon as we met I judged her to be kind and capable. Lucy seemed to take to her quickly.

I saw them in the park opposite our office whilst on my lunch break. I was having a five-minute cigarette-stroll with Angela. Their arrival was heralded by a speedy whooshing and whirring, accented with clattering clunks and clicks. The rattling wheels scattered the stone-chips as they hurtled round the corner, halting at the duck-feeding platform. Lucy was wrapped up in blankets, snug in the Spring air: a little bundle with only her face showing, and fluttering wisps of hair flaring out from beneath her woolly hat. Brenda was chattering away to Lucy, who was gurgling contentedly, bubbles of saliva glinting in the sunlight.

'Got to go,' I yelled merrily across at them, as I ground out my cigarette end, smashing it into the path with my boot.

I wanted to join their chatter, point out the birds and trees to Lucy, show her the shy crocuses that hinted at their violet and turmeric hues, yet to open their faces to the sky. But it seemed Brenda had already said it all.

I don't really know much about Brenda, and I don't feel I know her well enough to ask too many questions. It's the way she is with Lucy that matters. When I got back from work last Friday Lucy was giggling, sat plumply in the middle of the floor, with the shredded Yellow Pages all around her. There was wet digestive biscuit everywhere, even along the skirting boards. She's so endlessly fidgety and untidy. I could see she was wet, though it didn't seem to be bothering her, merry as she was in the midst of her messy mayhem. Brenda saved the day of course. In she swept with her J-cloth and cheery smiles, fixing it all up within a moment. Lucy's bath was running upstairs. I knew that next to it there'd be a fresh nappy and warmly ironed pyjamas and bed socks. I could smell the bubbles, and pictured the soft cloudiness of the steaming bathroom. I yearned for a soak, but obviously Lucy comes first. I could hear them up there, enjoying the warmth and liquid peace of the tub. I sat on Lucy's bean-bag, but I couldn't relax. I put my head back, trying to wriggle myself into its shifting shape. I got slimy bits of spat-out biscuit in my hair.

Angela said she thinks I'm jealous of Brenda, and I suppose in a way that might be true. She's so competent. I suppose it's easier when you can think to yourself, 'Well, at least I'm being paid to clean up this poo...' And Lucy can be delightful, so there's job satisfaction of a kind you don't get in office work. But it's a hard job she has, spending hours and hours with Lucy, and no adult conversation. No thank-yous. No answers. That's what I find hard.

Last Sunday was Brenda's day off. Lucy was in her little rocky-chair in the garden whilst I prepared the picnic. I took out the portable cassette player for her, and put on one of her favourite tapes. I think music is so important—they say that emotional response to music is one of the first centres to develop in a growing foetus' brain, and one of the last functions to fold at the other end of life. Lucy was in fine form, clapping her hands, her podgy knees wriggling with her laughter. I was busily mashing away at the eggs, squashing in the mayonnaise with a bent old fork, when I heard her wailing. Running out, I realised the music had stopped. I bent down to turn the tape over, and saw that all the buttons on top of the player were jammed. She must have been pushing them all in, ramming them down with her round hands, all at once. Opening it up to extract the cassette, I was met with about three metres of twisty spiralling untamed tape reel. The tape was one my Dad bought for her, before he died. Leaving it out of reach I headed back to the kitchen, desperately trying not to spoil things. Lucy was all grins again, smiling in the sunshine, watched by the irregular daffodils which swayed rather dementedly in the rising breeze.

Once I'd got the picnic ready we set forth on our outing to Bockerley Hill Picnic Area, a place that Dad often took us to last summer. He enjoyed superb health up to the last, his sturdy frame never for a moment hinting at such as swift exit. People said to me often—'Well, it's the best way to go, best not to linger…' One minute queueing at Freshley's for a bag of plums, and the next immobility and silence on the linoed floor, the blue flashing lights seen only by the startled onlookers. His heart just froze. Announced it was ceasing, and that nothing could be done to change its mind. A consolation, people said, that it was so quick. But how could I explain to Lucy why the loving man who sang her made-up songs as he dried her toes had disappeared? People seemed to assume she wouldn't notice. Brenda never even knew him. Now it's as if his ripples have reached the edge of the pond and there's no sign that he had ever touched it's surface. So my choice of Bockerley Hill was a way of sharing him again—just me, Lucy, and the gentle man who brought us both peace.

The journey was a bit hairy but we got there in one piece. I find it difficult to clamp Lucy's chair in situ on my own. All little levers and buckles and belts for her every comfort and security. Brenda can do it all in seconds, but with me it's all fingers and thumbs, broken nails and curses. Lucy screamed every time we stopped at a traffic light or junction, and I'd got a bit of a headache already—she's an expert at adjusting the pitch, tone, and volume of her wails for maximum discomfort to tired ears and tense minds. When I finally pulled into Bockerley's car park I turned in surprise at her silence. She was asleep. One of her shoes had fallen off. I picked it up, and sat there for a while, looking at her screwed up eyelids and the soft rise and fall of her milky round throat. Her head rolled slowly, and her cheek was lined where it had been pushed up against her collar. She looked a million years old. I remember reading of an extraordinary anthropological find that scientists had unearthed in dust-blown Africa. An ancient woman, perfectly preserved, scrunched up in her everlasting sleep, blind to the aeons of change and loss since she's last seen the sideways moon. The scientists called her 'Lucy'— this wrinkled slumbering specimen, excavated from the warm cradle of humankind. In the dog-barking car park at Bockerley Hill my own Lucy turned in her sleep, delighting in the inside world of her own unspoken dreams.

I didn't like to disturb her, but I was sure the sun wouldn't last much longer. I wanted us to have our lunch down by the little stream, in the sunlight, so I woke her gently, and she screeched. She squawked all the way down the rough gravel pathway, her wail accusing each time her chair bumped and lurched. I was exhausted, lugging the picnic stuff and man-handling her heavy chair round every pothole, over every waiting dog poo, stopping for every one of the staring Sunday trippers who were hell-bent on getting in our way. When we made it to the benches by the stream they were all full, so I parked Lucy near a willow, and fed her whilst on my knees. Hard little twigs poked at my legs and my feet became numb. We were outsiders, Lucy and I, sharing our yoghurt and our blackcurrant cordial. All the cosy little families, and all the full-of-hope-and-promise couples that gathered round the picnic tables sat on in judgement. Their indifference to the sight of me on my knees dripping stewed apple into Lucy's open mouth announced my separate-ness. Dad would have blended in. I got mud and grass stains all over my jeans and chocolate smears on my T-shirt. Lucy burped. And then it rained. And I'd forgotten her waterproofs. And then we took the wrong path. And then it took ages for me to find my keys under the soggy egg butties. And then there was a traffic jam. And then Lucy was sick.

When we finally got home I desperately wanted to flop into bed, but Lucy needed changing, and washing, and feeding again. I left her in the living room whilst I unloaded all our gear. I put the TV on, for some background noise. I only went outside for a moment, but that was enough. I entered the living room and saw her over in the corner. A small transistor radio which I keep on the low shelf by the video was in Lucy's hand. It has a long aerial, which she'd somehow managed to extend. And there she was, thrusting it at the telly. I don't even remember exactly what I did, or said, or felt. I only knew that Lucy was sobbing, her crumpled face showing agonies of betrayal and hurt as I stood over her, my hand raised, my palm stinging from where I'd slapped her. I realised I had actually hit her, hard. 'No,' I croaked, to Lucy, or to myself…and then I saw that Brenda had slunk in through the still-open front door, and was stood in the archway, looking. I knew she'd seen it all. In a sweep of an arm I'd fallen from a somewhat pitiable career woman to an out-of-control abuser. I ran to the kitchen, a blob of not knowing where to hide or stop it hurting. I heard Brenda calm Lucy.

I don't know what to do now. I've tried to bury myself in work, my tidy piles of paperwork to disguise my failure. I'm having such doubts now about Saint Brenda. Last night I heard them in the bathroom. Lucy was obviously being uncooperative and Brenda snapped at her, 'Now stop it!' she shouted. Lucy cried, her snivels eating my insides. 'Shut up!' Brenda yelled, her tone so very harsh. How harsh? Harder than my slap?

I sat with Lucy for a long time, once she was in bed. Tears ran down my face. I know I have let her down. How can I reprimand Brenda for shouting after she witnessed my own performance? Lucy's eyes met mine as I sat there, my one hand stroking her hair, the other wiping my wet cheeks. Oh Lucy. Poor suffering Lucy.

'I'll not leave you,' I said, 'You'll stay here with me 'til you can join Dad. I'll try my best, I promise…'

Lucy smiled. Lucy, my dear Mother.

Acknowledgements

'The Year the Flamingos Came' first appeared in *In Margate By Lunchtime* published by Cultured Llama

'The Lickspittle Leviathan' first appeared in *Sharkpunk* edited by Johnathan Green and published by Snowbooks Ltd.

All stories previously published at thanetwriters.com

Contributors

David Chitty was born and raised in Thanet. He is a writer who specialises in writing dark, transgressive fiction that has a comedic edge to it. He is also the Senior Editor for Thanet Writers. More of his work can be found at davidchitty.com

Rebecca Delphine writes fiction for young adults and enjoys clashing themes of romance and chaos. She lives in Cliftonville in Thanet.

Charles Dickens was an author and social critic who wrote over a dozen novels and novellas. Best known for his books *David Copperfield*, *Oliver Twist*, and *A Christmas Carol*, he used fiction to comment on social injustice. A frequent Thanet visitor, he based *Bleak House* on his residence in the area.

J A DuMairier is an author who was born and raised in Thanet, is London-based, and a journalist in another life; kept busy by two daughters and enjoys long walks in the countryside.

Luke Edley is a humorous fiction writer, poet and novelist who lives in Margate. Fond of satire, he is interested in comic novels, black comedy and tales of satirical derring-do.

Rosie Escott moved to Kent in 2005, when she came to study MA Film Production. She is the manager of a local arts organisation and works as a fundraiser for several other charities. She writes short stories and poems in her spare time. She is lucky enough to live on Margate seafront and never takes the sea and sunset views for granted.

Kirsty Louise Farley is a writer born and raised in Margate. She writes mostly in a macabre fashion with themes of heartbreak and mental health. Dog walks, open mics and friends take up most of her time when she isn't writing. She regularly updates fadedscribblings.tumblr.com with first drafts and notes to pose as teasers for final drafts to be showcased at gigs.

Ghillie is originally from Glasgow and is a poet and social commentator who has used past experiences as a basis for poetry. No matter what life throws, he believes that lurking somewhere nearby is a means of relating that in a colourful, meaningful and perhaps even a humorous way.

Janet Gogerty has been writing frantically for over ten years after joining a weekly writing group. She began writing short stories and then novels. She has published four novels and four story collections and writes regular blogs. Her interests include photography, reflected in her website, gardening and seaside life.

David Grimstone was encouraged to write from a young age by Sir Terry Pratchett and debuted alongside his hero in the fantasy anthology *Knights of Madness* just after his 19th birthday. He is now a bestselling author of series fiction for children, teenagers and young adults. His previous books include *The Illmoor Chronicles* (Disney), *Undead Ed* (Hodder), *Davey Swag*, *Gladiator Boy* (Hodder) and *Outcasts*, which have sold over a million copies worldwide and been translated into fifteen languages. He was born in Margate and lives in Ramsgate.

Maggie Harris is a Guyana-born poet and prose writer who lived in Thanet since 1972, attending UKC where she won the TS Eliot Prize for Poetry. Her poetry is influenced by both English lyricism and Caribbean rhythms. A prize-winner in both Guyana and the UK, her story collections are *Canterbury Tales on a Cockcrow Morning* and *In Margate by Lunchtime* (Cultured Llama), and *Writing on Water* (Seren). A ten-year sojourn in Wales has deepened her interest in history, migration and landscape, all reflected in her poetry collection *Sixty Years of Loving*.

Roger Jefferies writes fiction, short stories and novels. Several short stories have been published in the literary magazine 'Ariadne's Thread' and by Thanet Writers; a novel, *Ursula's Secrets*, was published as an ebook. His book of letters from the First World War found in a skip, *I Remain Your Loving Wife Lizzie*, was published in 2018 by Greenwich Exchange.

Sam Kaye is a writer and poet from the seaside town of Broadstairs. His writing focus is primarily aimed at his debut novel and cutting his teeth in the world of poetry and short stories. Sam has dived into the literary world head first and has recently joined the Thanet Writers team as a journalist and contributor. He loves a good ale, a fast film and things on two wheels.

Catherine Law was born in Harrow, Middlesex, and now lives 10 minutes from the sea in Margate. She worked as a secretary at the BBC before moving into the world of glossy magazines, where she was a sub-editor for over 20 years. But writing has always been her first love and in 2015, with three novels under her belt, she gave up her job to pursue her dream. Her fourth novel, *Map of Stars* (set in Kent during WW2), was published in 2016 and shortlisted for the Romantic Novelists Association Historical Novel award 2017. Her latest book, *The First Dance*, was published in 2018.

Lannah Marshall is a writer and illustrator frequently found at her keyboard, buried under notebooks, or lost in the many worlds found in the pages of her favourite authors.

John Mount is a writer, subeditor, film curator/programmer and script reader who lives in Ramsgate.

Matthew Munson is a life-long proud Thanetian and revels in the creativity of people in the area. He has had three novels published and appeared in two previous short story anthologies; this year sees the release of a novella. He currently lives in Thanet where he spends his time working on his four-book series, preparing for his next marathon, and advocating for invisible disabilities through the charity he co-founded, T2D.

Seb Reilly is a writer, fiction author and occasional musician from Thanet. He writes for various magazines. His website can be found at sebreilly.com

Connor Sansby is a poet, author, festival producer and Editor-in-Chief for Whisky & Beards Publishing. Since 2013, Connor has performed across the South of England, including Margate Soul Festival, Wise Words Festival and London's Let's Kill It. His work touches on themes of cultural waste, depression and the uncomfortable in the everyday. In 2016, Connor released his first short story collection, *I am Not a Well Person*. His first collection of poetry, *Promise Me the Journey Back*, will be released in 2018.

Alice Olivia Scarlett is the Fiction Editor for Thanet Writers. Her stories are about magic, sex, and history. She's a softcore feminist and hardcore stationery hoarder.

James Souze is a pseudonym for a local writer who, after a long hiatus, is exploring poetry again.

Sarah Tait is a Ramsgate poet, beach-walker, haiku-fan and nurse. An active member of the local poetry scene in Thanet, she has been writing poetry for many years and has had her work published in a variety of literary magazines. Her website is sarahtait01.wordpress.com

Stephanie Upton was born and raised in Broadstairs; her parents were well-known local teachers. She is retired and is working on becoming a foster carer. Stephanie now lives in Staffordshire, but regularly visits Thanet to see her family and friends, often attending community events where possible. 'Home is where the heart is,' and her heart is always in Thanet.

Thanet Writers is a trading name of Thanet Writers CIC, a Community Interest Company (CIC number: 10690420) based in Thanet, Kent, UK. Thanet Writers CIC is dedicated to supporting writers in and with a connection to Thanet, publishing writing with artistic or educational merit, and promoting literature, creativity and culture. Thanet Writers CIC is supported using public funding by the National Lottery through Arts Council England.

Thanet has a long literary heritage including connections to renowned writers such as Charles Dickens, Jane Austen, and T.S. Eliot. Thanet Writers was established to honour and continue that legacy. Working closely with writers, writers' groups and poetry groups, Thanet Writers aims to publish writing from authors and poets linked to Margate, Broadstairs, Ramsgate, and Thanet as a whole, raise awareness of literature, and offer and support community projects within Thanet and on a larger scale.

"Our mission is to promote the literary arts, writing and writers linked to Thanet, advance the education of the public in English Language, Literature, and Speaking and Listening, and to forward the engagement of writing and reading for the benefit of the community."

Thanet Writers CIC publish print anthologies of writing, both in physical and ebook form. The publication and release of print anthologies will expand the publishing potential of Thanet Writers, along with further promoting the artistic reputation of the local writing community and the authors and poets within it.

Copies are sold to generate funds for Thanet Writers CIC to further support the local writing and cultural community. These books are also provided free of charge to local libraries and educational establishments to actively encourage engagement with the arts.

thanetwriters.com was launched to promote literature and poetry, and publish essays and articles on writing craft. The site publishes short stories, poetry, literary essays, and book reviews, along with features and video content, all provided by writers with a link to Thanet.

Thanet Writers encourages and promotes public engagement with culture and the arts. New writers are published alongside experienced authors and poets, becoming part of a community, building confidence and boosting self-esteem, thereby facilitating a heightened sense of pride and achievement.

Supported using public funding by the National Lottery through Arts Council England.

For more information about the writers of Thanet, and to read their short stories, poetry, essays and book reviews, please visit:

thanetwriters.com